The Home Adventure Library 4

Great Stories From World Literature

COMPILED BY DORIS HEITKOTTER

Illustrated by John Everds and Lou Cunette

Holidays and Entertainments

BY BARBARA BROOKS AND RICHARD WHITTINGHAM

Illustrated by Joe Rogers

Index

The Southwestern Company

Nashville, Tennessee

Copyright © 1984, 1982, 1979, 1973, 1968 by
The Southwestern Company
Printed in the United States of America
R.R.D.

CONTENTS

Great Stories From World Literature

The Goose That Laid a Golden Egg	5
Rain, Rain, Go Away	6
If	6
Hey! Diddle Diddle	7
Hickory Dickory Dock	7
There Was a Little Girl	7
Old Mother Hubbard	8
The Man, the Boy, and the Donkey *Aesop*	10
The Sun and the Wind *Aesop*	12
The Three Golden Apples *A Wonder Book for Boys and Girls • Nathaniel Hawthorne*	13
Pinocchio Learns To Tell the Truth *Retold by Eugene Ehrlich*	19
The Frog Prince *Fairy Tales from Grimm • The Brothers Grimm*	28
The Nightingale *Danish Fairy Legends and Tales • Hans Christian Andersen*	35
The Ant and the Grasshopper *Aesop*	45
Mowgli's Brothers *The Jungle Book • Rudyard Kipling*	46
The Shooting Match at Nottingham *The Merry Adventures of Robin Hood • Howard Pyle*	55
Rapunzel, the Girl with the Golden Hair *Retold by Eugene Ehrlich*	65

The Hare and the Tortoise   74
    Aesop
Alice Meets Humpty Dumpty   75
    Alice's Adventures in Wonderland • Lewis Carroll
The Cat and the Pain-Killer   85
    The Adventures of Tom Sawyer • Mark Twain
Wynken, Blynken, and Nod   92
    Poems of Childhood • Eugene Field
Barbara Frietchie   94
    John Greenleaf Whittier

Holidays and Entertainments

AMERICAN HOLIDAYS
    New Year's Day   99
    Lincoln's Birthday   102
    Washington's Birthday   104
    Easter   107
    Memorial Day   110
    Independence Day   112
    Labor Day   114
    Halloween   116
    Thanksgiving   119
    Christmas   121

Holidays and
Entertainments *continued*

HOLIDAYS THROUGHOUT THE WORLD

Jewish Holidays 129

Moslem Holidays 133

European Holidays 136

Holidays in Great Britain 140

Holidays in Canada 143

Latin American Holidays 145

Chinese Holidays 150

Japanese Holidays 153

Holidays in India 157

PARTIES AND ENTERTAINING

Time for a Party 161

How To Be a Host or Hostess 163

Party Invitations 167

Party Food 168

Party Games 171

Decorations and Costumes 179

How To Be a Guest 186

Saying Thank You 190

Index 191

Great Stories From
World Literature

The Goose That Laid a Golden Egg

AESOP

"DEAR WIFE," said the farmer as he sat down to his breakfast, "I wish we didn't have to work so hard."

"I don't mind," said his wife. "We have enough to eat, clothes to wear, and a warm house."

"That's not enough for me," the farmer said. "I want to be rich."

After breakfast, the farmer's wife went out to the house where they kept their geese. There among the eggs the geese had laid was a yellow egg. She knew that something strange had happened and told her husband.

"Why this egg is made of gold," he said. "Show me which goose laid the egg."

They went out to look at the geese but they could not tell which goose had laid the golden egg.

"I know what to do," said the farmer. "I will kill the geese one by one until I find the one that has golden eggs inside."

"Why not be content to wait until it lays another golden egg? One golden egg will buy so much for us until we find the next one."

But the farmer couldn't fight his greed. He killed his geese one by one and found no more golden eggs. What's more, all his fine geese never again would lay eggs at all.

GREED CAN KILL THE GOOSE THAT LAYS A GOLDEN EGG.

RAIN, RAIN, GO AWAY

Rain, rain, go away,
Come again another day.
Little Johnny wants to play.

Mother Goose Rhymes

IF

If all the world were apple pie,
  And all the sea were ink,
And all the trees were bread and cheese,
  What should we have for drink?

HEY! DIDDLE DIDDLE

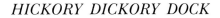

Hey! Diddle diddle,
The cat and the fiddle,
The cow jumped over the moon.
The little dog laugh'd
To see such sport
And the dish ran away with the spoon.

HICKORY DICKORY DOCK

Hickory dickory dock,
The mouse ran up the clock.
The clock struck one,
The mouse ran down.
Hickory dickory dock.

THERE WAS A LITTLE GIRL

There was a little girl who had a little curl
Right in the middle of her forehead.
When she was good, she was very, very good,
And when she was bad she was horrid.

Old Mother Hubbard

Old Mother Hubbard
Went to the cupboard,
To get her poor dog a bone:
But when she got there
The cupboard was bare,
And so the poor dog had none.

She went to the baker's
To buy him some bread,
But when she came back
The poor dog was dead.

She went to the joiner's
    To buy him a coffin,
But when she came back
    The poor dog was laughing.

She took a clean dish
    To get him some tripe,
But when she came back
    He was smoking a pipe.

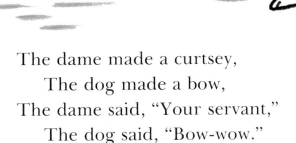

The dame made a curtsey,
    The dog made a bow,
The dame said, "Your servant,"
    The dog said, "Bow-wow."

This wonderful dog
    Was Dame Hubbard's delight;
He could sing, he could dance,
    He could read, he could write.

She gave him rich dainties
    Whenever he fed,
And built him a monument
    When he was dead.

SARAH CATHERINE MARTIN

The Man, the Boy, and the Donkey

AESOP

A MAN AND HIS SON were going with their donkey to market. As they were walking along, a countryman passed them and said, "You fools, what is a donkey for but to ride upon?"

So the man put the boy on the donkey and they went on their way. Soon they passed a group of men. One of them said, "See that lazy youngster? He lets his father walk while he rides."

So the man ordered his boy to get off, and got on himself. They hadn't gone far when they passed two women. One woman said to the other, "Shame on that

lazy lout, to let his poor little son trudge along beside that big, strong donkey!"

Well, the man didn't know what to do. At last he took his boy up before him on the donkey. By this time they had come to the town. The passersby began to jeer and point at them. The man stopped and asked what they were scoffing at. The men said, "Aren't you ashamed of yourself for overloading that poor donkey of yours—you and your hulking son?"

The man and the boy got off and tried to think what to do. They thought and they thought. At last they cut down a pole, tied the donkey's feet to it, and raised the pole and the donkey to their shoulders. They went along amid the laughter of all who met them till they came to Market Bridge. The donkey, getting one of his feet loose, kicked out and caused the boy to drop his end of the pole. In the struggle the donkey fell over the bridge. His forefeet being tied together, he was drowned.

"That will teach you," said an old man who had followed them:

PLEASE ALL, AND YOU WILL PLEASE NONE.

The Sun and the Wind

AESOP

THE WIND DECIDED one day that he was the strongest creature in the sky. As soon as the Sun came out that day, he said, "My friend the Sun, let's have a contest to see who is stronger?"

This idea did not seem very good to the kindly Sun, who had only just come out. "If you please, Wind, I would just as soon not do that. I have a long day ahead of me to spread my sunshine."

"I believe you know I am stronger than you. If you will just say that, I will find someone else to play this game with me."

At this the Sun became a bit annoyed with the Wind and decided after all that he would be willing to try his strength.

"How shall we play our game?" said the Sun.

"I know," said the Wind. "There's a traveler down below who is wearing a heavy coat. Let's see who can get that coat off the traveler's back. I'll go first."

The Wind blew and blew as hard as he could. But whenever the Wind blew, the traveler wrapped his coat tighter and tighter about him. Finally, the Wind could blow no more.

Then the Sun turned on his kindly rays and warmed the traveler up until the man had no need for his coat. Soon enough, the man took off his coat and carried it on his arm.

"You win," said the Wind, who had learned a lesson.

KINDLY ACTIONS CAN DO MORE THAN FORCE.

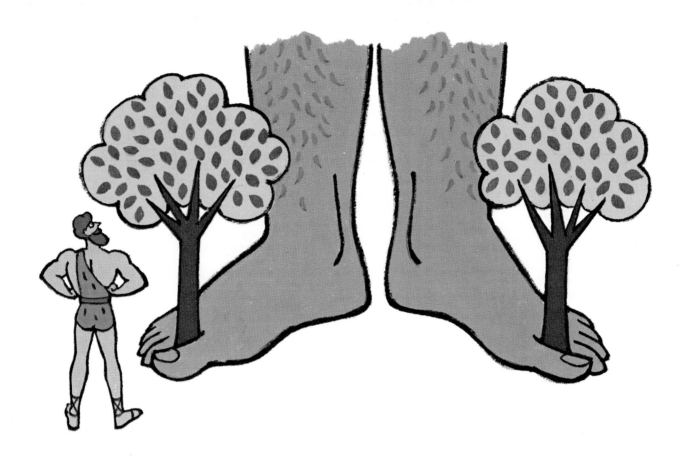

The Three Golden Apples

NATHANIEL HAWTHORNE

Hercules was a great hero, known both for his strength and kindness. In return for the King of Greece's promise not to harm his stepfather, Hercules became the King's slave for ninety-nine months. The king did not like Hercules and gave him twelve dangerous Labors to do. For one of these Labors, Hercules was told to bring back three golden apples from the garden of the Hesperides. It was a dangerous mission because any mortal who picked one of these apples would immediately die. Hercules traveled far to find the garden, and on his way some nymphs told him that he should ask for help from Atlas, the giant who holds up the sky.

THE GIANT WAS AS TALL as a mountain. So vast
was he that the clouds rested about his middle, like a
belt, and hung like a beard from his chin, and flitted
before his huge eyes, so that he could not see Hercules.
And, most wonderful of all, the giant held up his great
hands and appeared to support the sky, which so far as
Hercules could see, rested on his head!

Just then a breeze blew away the clouds from before
the giant's face. Poor fellow! He had evidently stood
there a long while. An ancient forest had been growing
and decaying around his feet, and oak trees six or seven
centuries old had sprung from the acorn and forced
themselves between his toes. The giant now looked
down from the far height of his great eyes, and seeing

Hercules, roared out in a voice that resembled thunder, "Who are you, down at my feet there?"

"I am Hercules," thundered back the hero. "And I am seeking for the garden of the Hesperides!"

"I am Atlas, the mightiest giant in the world! And I hold the sky upon my head."

"So I see," answered Hercules. "But can you show me the way to the garden of the Hesperides?"

"What do you want there?" asked the giant.

"I want three of the golden apples," shouted Hercules. "For my master the King."

"There is nobody but myself," quoth the giant, "that can go to the garden of the Hesperides and gather the apples. If it were not for this little business of holding up the sky, I would make half a dozen steps across the sea, and get them for you."

"Is the sky very heavy?" Hercules inquired.

"Why, not particularly so, at first," answered the giant, shrugging his shoulders. "But it gets to be after a thousand years!"

"And how long a time," asked the hero, "will it take you to get the golden apples?"

"Oh, that will be done in a few moments!" cried Atlas. "I will take ten or fifteen miles at a stride, and be at the garden and back again before your shoulders begin to ache."

"Well, then," answered Hercules, "I will climb the mountain behind you there, and relieve you of your burden." Without more words, the sky was shifted from the shoulders of Atlas and placed upon those of Hercules. Then Atlas stepped into the sea. His first stride covered ten miles. Hercules watched the giant as he went onward. It was a wonderful sight. But, as the gigantic shape faded entirely out of view, Hercules realized that the weight of the sky was already a little irksome to his shoulders.

"I really pity the poor giant," thought Hercules. "If it tires me so much in ten minutes, how it must have tired him in a thousand years."

I know not how long it was before, to his unspeakable joy, he beheld the huge shape of the giant. At his approach, Atlas held up his hand, in which Hercules could see three magnificent golden apples, as big as pumpkins, all hanging from one branch.

"I am glad to see you again," shouted Hercules. "So you have got the golden apples?"

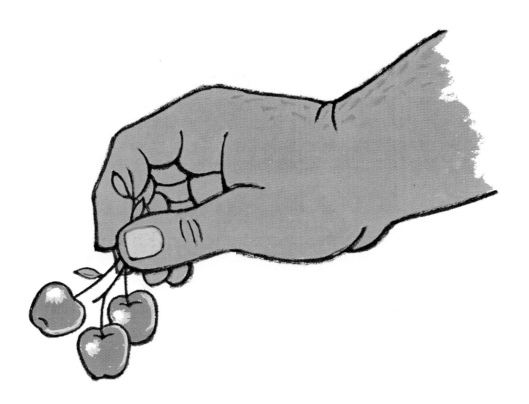

"Certainly," answered Atlas, "and very fair apples they are. I took the finest that grew on the tree, I assure you."

"You have had a pleasant ramble and I heartily thank you for your trouble," said Hercules, "and now, as I have a long way to go, and am rather in haste, will you be kind enough to take the sky off my shoulders again?"

"Why, as to that," said the giant, "I have no fancy for burdening myself with the sky just now."

"What!" shouted Hercules. "Do you intend to make me bear this burden forever?"

"We will see about that one of these days," answered the giant. "At all events, you ought not to complain if you have to bear it the next hundred years, or perhaps the next thousand. I bore it a good while longer, in spite of the backache. Well, then, after a thousand years, if I happen to feel in the mood, we may possibly shift about again. You are certainly a very strong man, and can never have a better opportunity to prove it."

Hercules, being as clever as he was strong, said to the giant, "Just take the sky upon your head one instant, will you? I want to make a cushion of my lion's skin for the weight to rest on. It really chafes me, and will cause unnecessary inconvenience in so many centuries as I am to stand here."

"That's no more than fair, and I'll do it!" said the giant. "For just five minutes, then, I'll take back the sky. Only for five minutes, remember! I have no idea of spending another thousand years as I spent the last. Variety is the spice of life, I say!"

Ah, the thick-witted old rogue of a giant! He threw down the golden apples and received back the sky from the head and shoulders of Hercules onto his own, where it rightly belonged. And Hercules picked up the three golden apples and set out on his journey homeward.

And there stands the giant to this day, or, at any rate, there stands a mountain as tall as he, which bears his name. And when the thunder rumbles we may imagine it to be the voice of the Giant Atlas, bellowing after Hercules who tricked him.

Pinocchio Learns To Tell the Truth

RETOLD BY EUGENE EHRLICH

IN A LITTLE TOWN IN ITALY, a long time ago, there lived an old man named Geppetto. For all his life Geppetto had worked as a carpenter. He had made fine furniture for rich men and women. He had built beautiful houses for many families. He once had even built a doll house for the young daughter of the King of Naples.

When Geppetto made that house, he built every bit of furniture for it. The tiny chairs and tables. A beautiful kitchen with all things needed for cooking. A living room with a couch and easy chairs. Bedrooms complete with beds and a dresser and closets.

Geppetto even made tiny dolls to live in the house. There was a mother doll, and there was a father doll. There was a little boy doll, and there was a little girl doll. All the dolls seemed so real to the Princess that she played with them for many years.

But that was long ago.

Now Geppetto was getting old. His hands were becoming stiff. His back often hurt when he worked for a time. And his eyes were not very strong. Geppetto knew that he would not be able to go on working for much longer. He would soon have to stop making furniture. He would have to stop building houses. He probably would never again build a doll house for a princess.

Geppetto knew he would one day have to spend his time sitting in his little house, taking walks whenever the sun was out, and talking with his old friends while they sat together and watched young people go by.

None of this made Geppetto sad, for he knew that everyone must get old. He also knew that he had saved much of the money he had made during his life. He would never have to worry about having enough to eat or having a warm bed to sleep in. But Geppetto was not really happy.

What made Geppetto just a little bit sad was that he had never married, so he had no children to comfort him in his old age. He had no daughter to talk with. He had no son to teach his trade to or take walks with through the town. Geppetto knew he would eat alone for the rest of his days.

"If only I had a daughter or a son," Geppetto said to himself one day.

"Why not me?" said a voice.

"Eh, what's that? Who said that? Is there someone here in my workshop who is hiding from me?"

"I'm not hiding. I'm over here in your woodpile."

Geppetto got up from his chair and went to the woodpile. No one was there. Geppetto thought to himself, "I'm getting old. I'm beginning to hear voices even though no one is speaking."

"No, you're not. I'm speaking."

Sure enough, the voice seemed to be coming from the woodpile. Geppetto went back to the woodpile and began to take out the pieces one by one and put them down on the floor. When he got to the bottom, sure enough, he heard the voice again.

"That's better," said the voice. "You don't know how uncomfortable it is to lie at the bottom of a woodpile. Take me out now."

Geppetto looked down at the last log in his woodpile. It looked just like all the other logs, but when Geppetto lifted it up, it spoke.

"Thank you, Geppetto."

"You're welcome, whoever you are."

"Whoever I am? If you'll put your carving knife to me, you'll soon find out that I'm a boy. And I'm going to be your boy."

At these words, Geppetto became very happy. "Is it possible," he thought, "that I finally will have a boy—a boy who will play happily, run errands for me, learn my trade, keep me company in my old age?"

Geppetto went to his workbench and prepared his carving knives and his sandpaper and his glue. When he had everything he needed, he put the log across his knees and set to work.

Geppetto worked the whole day and night through. He carved a head and a face and arms and legs and a sturdy body—all from the same log. And sure enough, when the first light of day appeared, Geppetto had finished his work. There was a boy, a beautiful boy with a head of black hair and blue eyes and a pointy nose, just like all the boys in the town.

And Geppetto called the boy Pinocchio.

Pinocchio was everything that Geppetto had wished for. He sang—as well as a wooden boy could—while Geppetto made breakfast. He danced—as well as a wooden boy could—while Geppetto washed the dishes. He clapped his hands with happiness when Geppetto built a bed for Pinocchio to sleep in.

Every day from then on, Geppetto and Pinocchio would take walks together through the town. When Geppetto stopped to have a chat with his friends, Pinocchio would play with any children who happened to be around.

When Geppetto needed firewood, Pinocchio would go off to the woods and pick up what was needed. When

22

Geppetto's shoes needed mending, Pinocchio would take them off to the cobbler. When Geppetto needed water for his cooking, Pinocchio would go to the town well to get it.

Pinocchio was eager to learn carpentry, and this made Geppetto happy. One by one Geppetto taught Pinocchio how to use all the tools a carpenter needs to build fine furniture, to build houses, to build doll houses. Pinocchio learned very quickly, and Geppetto knew that one day Pinocchio would be a first-class carpenter.

Soon Geppetto bought a fine hat for Pinocchio to wear—with a real feather in it. He bought Pinocchio a splendid jacket to wear. He even bought him shoes—one pair for everyday and a special pair for Sundays.

When Geppetto would go out for a walk with Pinocchio on a fine Sunday afternoon, all the townspeople would see them.

"How nice your boy looks in his new clothes," they would say.

"Geppetto, you should get yourself some new clothes too," they would say.

"Who is that handsome young man with you?" they would say.

The old man had never been happier in his life. He had a good son.

Geppetto and Pinocchio took all their meals together, and even though Pinocchio would go off to play with his friends after the evening meal, he would always be home before dark.

It happened that Pinocchio was off playing in the forest one day in midsummer, when the days were very long and the nights were very short. He had made friends with a rabbit, and on this day Pinocchio and the rabbit were playing tag together.

While Pinocchio was running away from the rabbit to keep from being tagged, Pinocchio tripped and fell. When he sat up, he found that he had fallen over a leather bag. He picked it up and looked inside.

"Oh my, there are three gold coins in this bag. I wonder whose they are."

The words were hardly out of his mouth when a beautiful Fairy Queen suddenly appeared before Pinocchio. She was dressed all in white and wore a golden crown on her head and carried a golden wand.

"What have you there, Pinocchio?"

"It's just a leather bag," he said, thinking that if he could keep the coins for himself, he could buy enough candy with the coins to eat candy for the rest of his life.

"Is there anything in the bag?" said the Fairy Queen.

"No, it's quite empty."

At this, the Fairy Queen waved her wand in the air, and Pinocchio's nose began to itch.

"Why did you wave your wand?" said Pinocchio.

"Touch your nose and see," she said.

Pinocchio's nose had grown to twice its regular size! No wonder it itched! "Oh my," said Pinocchio. "How will I ever be able to go around town with such a nose? All the other boys will laugh at me. The birds will sit on my nose—there's enough room for twelve sparrows. And what if a woodpecker starts to work on the tip of my nose? Please, please help me."

"Are you sure there is nothing in the leather bag?" said the Fairy Queen.

"No. I told you before. There's nothing in the bag."

The Fairy Queen waved her wand in the air again, and again Pinocchio's nose began to itch even more.

"Don't tell me," said Pinocchio. "I don't have to touch my nose again to know what's happened. I can see that my nose has grown even bigger than before. Why have you done this to me? Now I can have twenty-four sparrows on my nose."

"I shall ask you just once more," said the Fairy Queen. "Is there anything in the leather bag?"

"Yes, oh yes!" said Pinocchio, whose nose was now so long that he thought it would break off. "There are three gold coins in the bag."

"Are you sure there are only three?" said the Fairy Queen.

"Oh yes. I am sure there are only three. Please do not make my nose grow any bigger. I can hardly reach the end of it. How will I ever be able to blow my nose?"

The Fairy Queen smiled at this and said, "Pinocchio, I have been watching you ever since you came to live with Geppetto. You have been a good boy up until today. But when I put that leather bag in front of you in order to make you fall and find it, I was testing you. I wanted to know whether you would tell a lie. And you did. You not only told one lie, you told two. That is not a good way to behave."

Pinocchio began to cry—as well as a wooden boy could cry. "I promise you, I will never tell a lie again. I promise."

As soon as Pinocchio finished talking, his nose began to itch again, and he could tell that his nose was beginning to return to its normal size. He reached up to touch it and found that his nose was once again just the size that Geppetto had carved.

"Oh, thank you, Fairy Queen," said Pinocchio. "Thank you for giving me back my real nose."

"Don't thank me for that," she said. "If you have truly learned that you must never lie again, then you have much more to thank me for than just your nose. Geppetto could have trimmed your nose every day, but only you can be truthful and reliable."

"Take your leather bag," said Pinocchio. "I'm sure you will want to have it back so you can teach other boys not to lie."

"No," said the Fairy Queen. "You take it home with you and give it to the good Geppetto. He will find the best use for the three gold coins."

With these words, the Fairy Queen vanished—as suddenly as she had appeared. Pinocchio was quite alone in the forest. He put the bag in the pocket of the jacket Geppetto had bought him and hurried home.

As soon as he closed the door behind him, Pinocchio gave the three gold coins to Geppetto.

"Where did you get these, Pinocchio?"

"In the forest. A Fairy Queen gave them to me."

"For telling that story, my boy, you'll have to go to bed without your dinner."

Pinocchio began to cry—as well as a wooden boy could cry—and told Geppetto the whole story. But Geppetto, who didn't believe in fairies, said, "I believe you think you are telling the truth, but just to be sure, you'll have to go to bed without your dinner anyway. Tomorrow I will ask all the townspeople whether they know anything about this gold. If no one knows whose gold it is, I will buy food for the poor families in our town."

"Well," Pinocchio said to himself later while he was getting into his bed, "Geppetto may have punished me even though I told the truth, but that's better than watching my nose get bigger. I'll never again tell a lie."

The Frog Prince

JACOB AND WILHELM GRIMM

IN THE OLDEN TIME, when wishing was having, there lived a King whose daughters were all beautiful. But the youngest was so exceedingly beautiful that the Sun himself was enchanted every time she came out into the sunshine.

Near the castle of this King was a large and gloomy forest, and in the midst stood an old lime tree, beneath whose branches splashed a little fountain. So whenever it was very hot, the King's youngest daughter ran off into this wood, and sat down by the side of this fountain. When she was bored, she would often divert herself by

throwing a golden ball up in the air and catching it. And this was her favorite amusement.

Now one day it happened that when the Princess threw this golden ball into the air, it did not fall down into her hand, but on the grass. Then it rolled past her into the fountain. The King's daughter followed the ball with her eyes, but it disappeared beneath the water, which was so deep that no one could see to the bottom. She began to cry louder and louder. As she cried, a voice called out, "Why weepest thou, O King's daughter? Thy tears would melt even a stone to pity." And she looked around to the spot whence the voice came, and saw a frog stretching his thick ugly head out of the water.

"You old water-paddler," said she, "was it you that spoke? I am weeping for my golden ball which has slipped away from me into the water."

29

"Be quiet and do not cry," answered the Frog. "I can give thee good advice. But what wilt thou give me if I fetch thy plaything up again?"

"What will you have, dear Frog?" said she. "My dresses, my pearls and jewels, or the golden crown which I wear?"

The Frog answered, "Dresses, or jewels, or golden crowns are not for me. But if thou wilt love me, and let me be thy companion and playfellow, and sit at thy table, and eat from thy little golden plate, and drink out of thy cup, and sleep in thy little bed—if thou wilt promise me all these, then will I dive down and fetch up thy golden ball."

"Oh, I will promise you all," said she, "if only you will get me my ball." But she thought to herself, "What is the silly Frog chattering about? Let him remain in the water with his equals. He cannot mix in society." But the Frog, as soon as he had received her promise, drew his head under the water and dived down. Presently he swam up again with the ball in his mouth, and threw it on the grass. The King's daughter was full of joy when she again saw her beautiful plaything. Taking it up, she ran off immediately.

"Stop! stop!" cried the Frog. "Take me with thee. I can't run as thou canst." But his croaking was useless. Although it was loud enough, the King's daughter did not hear it. Hastening home, she soon forgot the poor Frog, who was obliged to leap back into the fountain.

The next day, when the King's daughter was sitting at table with her father and all his courtiers, and was eating from her own little golden plate, something was

heard coming up the marble stairs, *splish-splash, splish-splash*. When it arrived at the top, it knocked at the door, and a voice said, "Open the door, thou youngest daughter of the King!"

She rose and went to see who it was that called her. But when she opened the door and caught sight of the Frog, she shut it again, and sat down at the table, looking very pale. But the King saw that her heart was beating violently, and asked her whether it were a giant who had come to fetch her away who stood at the door. "Oh, no!" she answered. "It is no giant, but an ugly Frog."

"What does the Frog want with you?" said the King.

"Oh, dear father, when I was sitting yesterday playing by the fountain, my golden ball fell into the water. This Frog fetched it up again because I cried so much, but first I must tell you, he pressed me so much, that I promised him he should be my companion. I never thought he could come out of the water, but somehow he has jumped out, and now he wants to come in here."

At that moment there was another knock, and a voice said:

> "King's daughter, youngest,
> Open the door.
> Hast thou forgotten
> Thy promises made
> At the fountain so clear?
> 'Neath the lime-tree's shade?
> King's daughter, youngest,
> Open the door."

Then the King said, "What you have promised, that you must perform. Go and let him in." So the King's daughter went and opened the door. The Frog hopped in after her right up to her chair.

As soon as she was seated the Frog said, "Take me up." But she hesitated so long that at last the King ordered her to obey. And as soon as the Frog sat on the chair he jumped on to the table and said, "Now push thy plate near me, that we may eat together." And she

did so, but as everyone saw, very unwillingly. The Frog seemed to relish his dinner much, but every bite that the King's daughter ate nearly choked her, till at last the Frog said, "I have satisfied my hunger and feel very tired. Wilt thou carry me upstairs now into thy chamber, and make thy bed ready that we may sleep together?" At this speech the King's daughter began to cry, for she was afraid of the cold Frog, and dared not touch him. Besides, he actually wanted to sleep in her own beautiful, clean bed.

But her tears only made the King angry. He said, "He helped you in the time of your trouble, and must not now be despised!"

So she took the Frog up with two fingers, and put him in a corner of her chamber. But as she lay in her bed, he crept up to it, and said, "I am so very tired that I shall sleep well. Do take me up or I will tell thy father."

This speech made the King's daughter terribly angry. Catching the Frog up, she threw him with all her strength against the wall, saying, "Now will you be quiet, you ugly Frog!"

But as he fell he was changed from a frog into a handsome Prince with beautiful eyes. After a little while, he became, with her father's consent, her dear companion and betrothed. Then he told her how he had been transformed by an evil witch, and that no one but herself could have had the power to take him out of the fountain. And soon they were married and went together into the Prince's own kingdom.

The Nightingale

HANS CHRISTIAN ANDERSEN

THE EMPEROR'S PALACE was the most magnificent palace in the world. It was made entirely of fine porcelain. The choicest flowers were to be seen in the garden. Everything in the Emperor's garden was excellently well-arranged. Whoever walked beyond it, however, came to a beautiful wood with very high trees, and beyond that, to a lake. Large vessels could sail close under the branches. Among the branches dwelt a Nightingale, who sang so sweetly that even the poor fisherman, who had so much else to do, would stand still and listen. "Oh, how pretty that is!" he would say, and then go back to his work.

Travellers came from all parts of the world to see the Emperor's city, the palace, and the garden. But if they heard the Nightingale, they said, "This is the best of all." Learned men wrote books about the city, the palace, and the garden. Nor did they forget the Nightingale. She was praised above everything else.

These books reached the Emperor. He read and read, and nodded his head. These splendid descriptions of the city, the palace, and the garden pleased him greatly. "But there is nothing like the Nightingale," said the book.

"What in the world is this?" said the Emperor. "The Nightingale! I do not know it at all! Can there be such a bird in my empire, in my garden even, without my having heard of it? Truly, one may learn something from books."

So he called his Gentleman Usher, who was so grand a personage that no one of inferior rank might speak to him. "There is said to be a very remarkable bird here, called the Nightingale," said the Emperor. "Her song, they say, is worth more than anything else in all my dominions. Why has no one ever told me of her?"

"I have never before heard her mentioned," said the Gentleman Usher. "She has never been presented at court."

"I wish her to come and sing before me this evening," said the Emperor. "The whole world knows what I have, and I do not know it myself. I wish to hear the Nightingale. She must be here this evening. If she doesn't come, after supper the whole court will be flogged."

"Tsing-pe!" exclaimed the Gentleman Usher. He ran upstairs and downstairs, and half the court ran with him. No one would have relished the flogging. Many were the questions asked about the wonderful Nightingale, whom the whole world talked of, and about whom no one at the court knew anything.

At last they met a poor little girl in the kitchen, who said, "Oh, yes, the Nightingale! I know her very well.

Oh, how she can sing! Every evening, when I rest in the wood, I hear her. It makes the tears come into my eyes."

"Little Kitchen-maiden," said the Gentleman Usher, "will you conduct us to the Nightingale? She is expected at court this evening."

So they went together to the wood, where the Nightingale was accustomed to sing.

"There she is!" said the little girl. "Listen! listen! There she sits." She pointed to a little gray bird up in the branches.

"Most excellent Nightingale," said the Gentleman Usher, "I have the honor to invite you to a court festival, which is to take place this evening. His Imperial Majesty will doubtless be enchanted with your delightful song."

"With the greatest pleasure," replied the Nightingale, "but my song would sound far better among the green trees." However, she followed willingly because she knew that the Emperor wished it.

In the midst of the grand hall, where the Emperor sat, a golden perch was erected on which the Nightingale was to sit.

And the Nightingale sang so sweetly that tears came into the Emperor's eyes. She sang more sweetly still, and tears rolled down his cheeks.

The Nightingale's success was complete. She was now to remain in court.

One day a large parcel arrived for the Emperor, on which was written, "Nightingale."

"Here we have another new book about our far-famed bird," said the Emperor. But it was not a book. It was a little piece of mechanism, lying in a box. It was

an artificial nightingale, which was intended to look like the living one. But it was covered all over with diamonds, rubies, and sapphires. When this artificial bird had been wound up, it could sing one of the tunes that the real Nightingale sang.

"Now they shall sing together. We will have a duet," said everyone. And so they must sing together. But it did not succeed, for the real Nightingale sang in her own way, and the artificial bird produced its tones by wheels. "It is not his fault," said the artist. "He keeps exact time and quite according to the method."

So the artificial bird must sing alone. He was quite
as successful as the real Nightingale. And then he was
so much prettier to look at. His plumage sparkled with
jewels. His silver and gold tail moved up and down.

Thirty-three times he sang one and the same tune,
and yet he was not weary. Everyone would willingly have
heard him again. However, the Emperor now wished the
real Nightingale to sing something—but where was she?
No one had remarked that she had flown out of the
open window—flown away to her own green wood.

"What is the meaning of this?" said the Emperor.
All of the courtiers abused the Nightingale and called
her a most ungrateful creature. "We have the best bird,
at all events," they said. And for the thirty-fourth time
they heard the same tune. The artist praised the bird
inordinately and received permission to show the bird
to the people on the following Sunday. But the fisherman, who had heard the real Nightingale, said, "It sounds

very pretty, almost like the real bird. But yet there is something wanting—I know not what."

The real Nightingale was banished from the empire.

The artificial bird had his place on a silken cushion, close to the Emperor's bed. His place was number one on the left side. For the Emperor thought that the side where the heart was situated must be the place of honor, and the heart is situated on the left side of an Emperor, as well as with other folks.

Thus it went on for a whole year. But one evening there was suddenly a noise, "Bang!" inside the bird. Then something sprang, "Sur-r-r." All the wheels were running about, and the music stopped.

The Emperor quickly jumped out of bed, and had his chief physician called. But what good could he be? Then the clockmaker was called. At last, after a great deal of discussion and consultation, the bird was in some measure put to rights again. But the clockmaker said he must be spared much singing. Now the artificial bird was allowed to sing only once a year.

When five years were passed, a great sadness visited the whole empire. In their hearts the people thought highly of their Emperor, and now he was ill. It was reported he could not live. A new Emperor had already been chosen, and the people stood in the street outside the palace.

Cold and pale lay the Emperor in his magnificent bed. A window was opened above and the moon shone down on the Emperor and the artificial bird.

The poor Emperor could scarcely breathe. It appeared to him as though something were sitting on his chest. He opened his eyes, and saw that it was Death, who had put on the Emperor's crown.

"Music, music!" cried the Emperor. "Thou dear little artificial bird! Sing, I pray thee, sing! I have given thee gold and precious stones. Sing, I pray thee, sing."

But the bird was silent. There was no one there to wind him up. Death continued to stare at the Emperor with his great hollow eyes. Everywhere it was still, fearfully still!

All at once the sweetest song was heard from the window. It was the little living Nightingale who was

sitting on a branch outside. She had heard of the Emperor's severe illness, and came to sing to him of comfort and hope. As she sang, the blood flowed more quickly through the Emperor's feeble limbs, and even Death listened and said, "Go on, little Nightingale, go on."

"Wilt thou give me the splendid gold Crown of the Emperor?" And Death gave up this treasure for a song. And the Nightingale sang on as Death flew out at the window like a cold, white shadow.

"Thanks, thanks!" said the Emperor. "Thou heavenly little bird, I know thee well! I have banished thee from my realm, and thou hast sung away death from my heart. How shall I reward thee?"

"Thou hast already rewarded me," said the Nightingale. "I have seen tears in thine eyes, as when I sang to thee for the first time. Those I shall never forget. They are jewels which do so much good to a minstrel's heart. But sleep now, and wake fresh and healthy. I will sing thee to sleep."

And she sang—and the Emperor fell into a sweet sleep. Oh, how soft and kindly was that sleep!

The sun shone in at the window when he awoke, strong and healthy. Not one of his servants had returned, for they all believed him dead. But the Nightingale still sat and sang.

The attendants came to look at their dead Emperor, and the Emperor said, "Good morning!"

The Ant and the Grasshopper

AESOP

ALL DAY LONG all through the warm days of summer, a green grasshopper went happily about. Whenever the grasshopper was thirsty, he would sip nectar from any plant he saw.

One afternoon, as the grasshopper was leaping from flower to flower, he saw beneath him a little black ant struggling to carry a fat leaf bigger than himself.

"Little friend," said the grasshopper, "what are you doing down there?"

"Why, I am carrying this leaf off to my nest. I must fill my nest with food to last through winter."

"Winter?" said the grasshopper. "Who cares about winter? Why don't you climb up to this flower and enjoy its sweet nectar? Winter will take care of itself."

"That isn't the way things work in this world," said the ant. "Winter will be here soon. The flowers will be gone, and there will be nothing to eat."

"Well, suit yourself," said the grasshopper. And off he went, singing happily and having no cares at all.

The ant returned to his work. It took all his strength to carry each leaf, but he did not mind. He knew he would have enough to last the winter.

Soon the cold weather came. The ant was snug in his nest with plenty of food to eat. The grasshopper? He had nothing to eat and soon was no more.

A WISE PERSON KNOWS THAT SUMMER DOES NOT LAST FOREVER.

Mowgli's Brothers

RUDYARD KIPLING

FATHER WOLF LISTENED. Below in the valley that ran down to a little river, he heard the dry, angry, snarly, singsong whine of a tiger. "The fool!" said Father Wolf. "To begin a night's work with that noise!"

"H'sh! It is neither bullock nor buck he hunts to-night," said Mother Wolf. "It is Man."

"Man!" said Father Wolf, showing all his teeth. "Faugh! Are there not enough beetles and frogs in the tanks that he must eat Man, and on our ground too!"

The purr grew louder, and ended in the full-throated "Aaarh!" of the tiger's charge.

Then there was a howl—an untigerish howl—from Shere Khan. "He has missed," said Mother Wolf. "What is it?"

Father Wolf ran out a few paces. "The fool had no more sense than to jump at a woodcutter's camp fire, and has burned his feet," said Father Wolf, with a grunt.

"Something is coming up hill," said Mother Wolf, twitching one ear. "Get ready."

The bushes rustled a little in the thicket, and Father Wolf dropped with his haunches under him, ready for his leap. He jumped—and then stopped in mid-spring.

"Man!" he snapped. "A man's cub. Look!"

Directly in front of him, holding on by a low branch, stood a naked brown baby who could just walk. He looked up into Father Wolf's face and laughed. "Is that a man's cub?" said Mother Wolf. "I have never seen one. Bring it here."

Father Wolf's jaws closed right on the child's back, and not a tooth even scratched the skin as he laid it down among the cubs.

"How little! How naked and—how bold!" said Mother Wolf, softly. The baby was pushing his way between the cubs to get close to the warm hide. "So this is a man's cub. Now, was there ever a wolf that could boast of a man's cub among her children?"

"I have heard now and again of such a thing, but never in our Pack or in my time," said Father Wolf. "He is altogether without hair, and I could kill him with a touch of my foot. But see, he looks up and is not afraid."

The moonlight was blocked out of the mouth of the cave, for Shere Khan's great square head and shoulders were thrust into the entrance. Father Wolf was very angry. "What does Shere Khan need?" he growled.

"My quarry. A man's cub went this way," said Shere Khan. "Its parents have run off. Give it to me."

Father Wolf knew that the mouth of the cave was too narrow for a tiger to come in by. "The wolves are a free people," said Father Wolf. "They take orders from the Head of the Pack, and not from any striped cattle-killer. The man's cub is ours—to kill if we choose."

"Ye choose and ye do not choose! What talk is this of choosing? By the bull that I killed, am I to stand nosing into your dog's den for my fair dues? It is I, Shere Khan, who speak!"

The tiger's roar filled the cave with thunder. Mother Wolf shook herself clear of the cubs and sprang forward, her eyes, like two green moons in the darkness, facing the blazing eyes of Shere Khan.

"And it is I, Raksha the Demon, who answer. The man's cub is mine. He shall not be killed. He shall live to run with the Pack and to hunt with the Pack. And in the end, look you, hunter of little naked cubs—he shall hunt thee! Now get thee hence! Go!"

Shere Khan might have faced Father Wolf, but he could not stand up against Mother Wolf, for he knew that where she was she had all the advantage of the

ground, and would fight to the death. So he backed out of the cave-mouth growling, and when he was clear he shouted:

"Each dog barks in his own yard! We will see what the Pack will say to this fostering of man-cubs. The cub is mine, and to my teeth will come in the end, O bush-tailed thieves!"

Mother Wolf threw herself down panting among the cubs, and Father Wolf said to her gravely:

"Shere Khan speaks this much truth. The cub must be shown to the Pack."

The Law of the Jungle lays down very clearly that any wolf may, when he marries, withdraw from the Pack he belongs to. But as soon as his cubs are old enough to stand on their feet he must bring them to the Pack Council, which is generally held once a month at full moon, in order that the other wolves may identify them. After that, the cubs are free to run as they please.

Father Wolf waited till his cubs could run a little, and then on the night of the Pack Meeting took them, and Mowgli the man-cub, and Mother Wolf to the Council Rock. Akela, the great, gray Lone Wolf, who led all the Pack by strength and cunning, lay out at full length on his rock, and below him sat forty or more wolves of every size and color. There was very little talking at the rock. The cubs tumbled over each other in the center of the circle where their mothers and fathers sat. Sometimes a mother wolf would push her cub far out into the moonlight, to be sure that he had not been overlooked. Akela from his rock would cry, "Ye know the Law—ye know the Law. Look well, O Wolves!"

And the anxious mothers would take up the call, "Look—look well, O Wolves!"

At last Father Wolf pushed Mowgli, called "the Frog," into the center, where he sat laughing and playing with some pebbles that glistened in the moonlight.

Akela never raised his head from his paws, but went on with the monotonous cry, "Look well!" A muffled roar came up from behind the rocks—the voice of Shere Khan crying, "The cub is mine. Give him to me. What have the Free People to do with a man's cub?"

Akela never even twitched his ears. All he said was, "Look well, O Wolves! What have the Free People to do with the orders of any save the Free People? Look well!"

There was a chorus of deep growls, and a young wolf in his fourth year flung back Shere Khan's question. "What have the Free People to do with a man's cub?"

Now the Law of the Jungle lays down that if there is any dispute as to the right of a cub to be accepted by the Pack, he must be spoken for by at least two members of the Pack who are not his father and mother.

"Who speaks for this cub?" said Akela. "Among the Free People who speaks?" There was no answer, and Mother Wolf got ready for what she knew would be her last fight, if things came to fighting.

Then the only other creature who is allowed at the Pack Council—Baloo, the sleepy brown bear who teaches the wolf cubs the Law of the Jungle—rose up on his hindquarters and grunted. "I speak for the man's cub. There is no harm in a man's cub. Let him run with the Pack, and be entered with the others. I myself will teach him."

"We need yet another," said Akela. "Baloo has spoken. Who speaks besides Baloo?"

A black shadow dropped down into the circle. It was Bagheera the inky black panther. Everybody knew Bagheera, and nobody cared to cross his path, for he was as cunning as a jackal, as bold as a wild buffalo, and as reckless as a wounded elephant. But he had a voice as soft as wild honey dripping from a tree.

"O Akela, and ye the Free People," he purred, "I have no right in your assembly, but the Law of the Jungle says that if there is doubt which is not a killing matter in regard to a new cub, the life of that cub may be bought at a price. And the law does not say who may or may not pay that price. Am I right?"

"Good! Good!" said the young wolves, who are always hungry. "Listen to Bagheera. The cub can be bought for a price. It is the Law."

Bagheera continued, "To kill a naked cub is shame. Besides, he may make better sport for you when he is grown. Baloo has spoken in his behalf. Now to Baloo's word I will add one bull, and a fat one, newly killed, not half a mile from here, if ye will accept the man's cub."

There was a clamor of scores of voices saying, "What matter? He will die in the winter rains. He will scorch in the sun. What harm can a naked frog do us? Let him run with the Pack. Where is the bull, Bagheera? Let him be accepted."

Shere Khan roared in the night, for he was very angry that Mowgli had not been handed over to him.

"Ay, roar well," said Bagheera, under his whiskers, "for the time comes when this naked thing will make thee roar to another tune, or I know nothing of man."

"It was well done," said Akela. "Men and their cubs are very wise. He may be a help in time. Take him away," he said to Father Wolf, "and train him as befits one of the Free People."

And that is how Mowgli was entered into the See-onee wolf pack, at the price of a bull and on Baloo's good word.

The Shooting Match
at Nottingham

HOWARD PYLE

WHEN ROBIN HOOD first heard the news, he was in Lincoln Town. Hastening back to Sherwood Forest, he soon called all his merry men about him and spoke to them thus:

"Now hearken, my merry men all, to the news that I have brought from Lincoln Town today. Our friend the Sheriff of Nottingham hath proclaimed a shooting match and hath sent messengers to tell of it through all the countryside. The prize is to be a bright golden arrow. Now I would have one of us win it, both because of the fairness of the prize and because our friend the Sheriff

55

hath offered it. So we will take our bows and shafts and go there to shoot, for I know right well that merriment will be a-going. What say ye, lads?"

Then young David of Doncaster spoke up and said, "Listen, I pray thee, good master, unto what I say. This knavish Sheriff hath laid a trap for thee in this shooting match and wishes nothing so much as to see thee there. So go not, good master, for I know well he doth seek to beguile thee. Stay within the greenwood lest we all meet dole and woe."

"Now," quoth Robin, "thou art a wise lad, and keepest thine ears open and thy mouth shut, as becometh a wise and crafty woodsman. But shall we let it be said that the Sheriff of Nottingham did cow bold Robin Hood

and his sevenscore as fair archers as are in all merry England? Nay, good David, what thou tellest me maketh me to desire the prize even more than I else should do. Therefore we must meet guile with guile. Now some of you clothe yourselves as rustic peasants, and some as tinkers, or as beggars. But see that each man taketh a good bow, in case need should arise. As for myself, I will shoot for this same golden arrow. How like you the plan, my merry men all?"

"Good, good!" cried all the band heartily.

A fair sight was Nottingham Town on the day of the shooting match. And never was such a company of yeoman as were gathered that day, for the very best archers of merry England had come to this match.

When the Sheriff and his dame had sat down, he bade his herald sound three blasts that came echoing cheerily back from the gray walls of Nottingham. The archers stepped forth to their places. Then the herald stood forth and loudly proclaimed the rules of the game as follows:

"One arrow shooteth each man first, and from all the archers shall the ten that shooteth the fairest shafts be choosen for to shoot again. Of these ten, shall the

three that shoot the fairest shafts be chosen for to shoot again. Three arrows shooteth each man of those three, and to him that shooteth the fairest shafts shall the prize be given."

Now the archers shot, each man in turn, and the good folk never saw such archery as was done that day. When the last arrow sped and struck the target, all the people shouted aloud, for it was noble shooting.

And now but ten men were left of all those that had shot before. Of these ten, six were famous throughout the land.

Then the Sheriff leaned forward, looking keenly among the archers to find whether Robin Hood was among them, but no one was there clad in Lincoln green, such as Robin and his band wore. "Now," quoth he to a man-at-arms who stood near him, "seest thou Robin Hood among those ten?"

"Nay, that do I not, your Worship," answered the man. "Six of them I know right well. Of the others, one is too tall and the other too short for that bold knave. Robin's beard is as yellow as gold, while yon tattered beggar in scarlet hath a beard of brown, besides being blind of one eye."

"Then," quoth the Sheriff, smiting his thigh angrily, "yon knave is a coward as well as a rogue, and dares not show his face among good men and true."

And now but three men were left of all those that had shot before. "Now shoot thou well, Gilbert," cried the Sheriff, "and if thine be the best shaft, fivescore broad silver pennies will I give to thee beside the prize."

"Truly, I will do my best," quoth Gilbert. So saying, he drew forth a fair smooth arrow and, drawing his bow with care, he sped the shaft. Straight flew the arrow and lit fairly in the clout, a finger's breadth from the center.

"Now, by my faith," cried the Sheriff, "that is a shrewd shot!"

Then the tattered stranger stepped forth, and all the people laughed as they saw a yellow patch that showed beneath his arm when he raised his elbow to shoot, and also to see him aim with but one eye. He drew the good

yew bow quickly, and quickly loosed a shaft. So short was the time that no man could draw a breath betwixt the drawing and the shooting. Yet his arrow lodged nearer the center than the other by twice the length of a barleycorn.

Then Adam o' the Dell shot, carefully and cautiously, and his arrow lodged close beside the stranger's. After a short space they all three shot again, and once more

the tattered stranger's shot was the best. Then after another time of rest, they all shot for the third time. This time Gilbert took great heed to his aim, keenly measuring the distance and shooting with shrewdest care. Straight flew the arrow, and the shaft lodged close beside the spot that marked the very center.

"Well done, Gilbert!" cried the Sheriff right joyously. "Now, thou ragged knave, let me see thee shoot a better shaft than that!"

Nought spoke the stranger but took his place. He drew his trusty yew, holding it drawn but a moment, then loosed the string. Straight flew the arrow, and so

61

true that it smote a gray goose feather from off Gilbert's shaft, which fell fluttering through the sunlit air as the stranger's arrow lodged in the very center. No one spoke a word for a while and no one shouted, but each man looked into his neighbor's face amazedly.

"Nay," quoth old Adam o' the Dell presently, drawing a long breath and shaking his head as he spoke, "I shoot no more today, for no man can match with yon stranger, whosoe'er he may be."

Then the Sheriff came down and drew near, in all his silks and velvets, to where the tattered stranger stood leaning upon his stout bow. "Here, good fellow," quoth the Sheriff, "take thou the prize, and well and fairly hast thou won it, I trow. What may be thy name, and whence comest thou?"

"Men do call me Jock o' Teviotdale, and thence am I come," said the stranger.

"Then, by Our Lady, Jock, thou art the fairest archer that e'er mine eyes beheld, and if thou wilt join my service, I will clothe thee with a better coat than thou hast

upon thy back. Thou shalt eat and drink of the best. I
trow thou drawest better bow than that same coward
knave Robin Hood. Say, good fellow, wilt thou join my
service?"

"Nay, that I will not," quoth the stranger roughly.
"I will be mine own, and no man in all merry England
shall be my master."

"Then get thee gone, and a plague seize thee!"
cried the Sheriff, and his voice trembled with anger.
"And by my faith I have a good part of a mind to have
thee beaten for thine insolence!" He turned upon his
heel and strode away.

Then did Robin and his merry men return to Sherwood Forest. Amidst much laughter, he took the patch from off his eye and stripped away the scarlet rags from off his body and showed himself all clothed in fair Lincoln green.

But Robin Hood took Little John aside and said, "Truly am I vexed, for I heard the Sheriff say today, 'Thou shootest better than that coward knave Robin Hood, that dared not show his face here this day.' I would fain let him know who it was won the golden arrow—and that I am no coward."

Little John said, "Good master, I will send yon fat Sheriff news of all this by a messenger such as he doth not expect."

That day as the Sheriff sat at meat in the great hall of his house, an arrow came through the open window and landed on the dinner table. A fine scroll was tied to it. The Sheriff opened the scroll and glanced at it while the veins upon his forehead swelled and his cheeks grew ruddy with rage, for this is what he saw:

"Now Heaven bless thy Grace this day
    Say all in Sweet Sherwood,
For thou didst give the prize away
    To merry Robin Hood."

Rapunzel, the Girl with the Golden Hair

RETOLD BY EUGENE EHRLICH

A LONG TIME AGO, there lived a man and a woman who, though married for many years, had never had a child of their own. How they longed to hear the voice of a little daughter or son, to watch a child grow up in their home, to share the happiness of that child.

But it seemed, after they had been married for a long time, that they never were to have a child. After a while they never spoke of the matter. Each of them carried the secret wish alone.

Behind the house in which the couple lived was a beautiful forest, and out of that forest they had cleared

65

a small place in which they planted their garden each year. They would have fine red tomatoes and orange carrots and pure-white cauliflower and every other vegetable they needed. But the vegetable they liked best was the lettuce they planted each year.

One day in spring, when the lettuce was just beginning to grow large enough to pick, the husband said to his wife, "I think that today would be a good time to have a fine lunch with lettuce salad, don't you?"

The wife needed little encouragement. She had been watching the lettuce since the first day the young plants had poked their heads through the soil. She knew that the tender leaves would be just right to eat. Thinking about the olive oil she had made the year before and the red vinegar she had bought just the day before, the wife went out into the garden, all the while singing to herself.

In no time at all she was out among her lettuce plants, picking a leaf here and a leaf there, careful not to hurt any of her precious plants.

Suddenly she saw a group of plants she knew she had not planted. She tugged at one of the plants, and it came up easily in her hand. "I wonder what plant that is," she thought. She tasted the white root. "Why, I don't know this plant at all, but it certainly tastes good. I think it will go well in our salad."

When her husband sat down to lunch, he was hungry. He had cut a lot of wood that morning and had hauled it back to the house and stacked it in his woodshed.

"Now, that's what I call a good salad. I'll have a slice of your fresh bread, some salad, and a bowl of hot soup, and that will send me back to my work feeling good."

His wife spooned a portion of salad onto her husband's plate and waited to hear his comment.

"Delicious. Truly delicious, my good wife. But what's that I taste in the salad? It's too early for onions, but whatever you have added to the lettuce gives this salad just the right flavor."

The wife got up from the table and went to the cupboard where she had stored the strange root she had used in the salad.

Coming back to the table, she put the root in front of him and said, "This is what you taste. I don't know what it is, but I am sure you do."

"Why of course, that's campion, or *rapunzel* as it is called by the old people. I didn't know you had planted it. Where did you find the seed?"

"I didn't plant the rapunzel," she said. "It came up all by itself in the garden, and I am glad."

"So am I. Is there any more out there?"

"Oh yes," she said, "there's enough for many more salads. Aren't we lucky?"

"I should say. This is our lucky day, dear wife."

Soon enough lunch was over. The man went out to work some more in the forest, and the woman set about her chores. She saved the garden for last, as she always did, because garden work was her favorite. If she worked first in the garden, she knew, she would want to stay out there so long that her other work would never get done.

Finally her chores in the house were done, and the woman went out to the garden. And while she was on her knees, pulling weeds from the bed of rapunzel, she thought she heard a voice.

"That's strange. Who could possibly be calling to me now?" Thinking the voice was just something she imagined, she bent back to her work.

Suddenly she heard the voice again, and this time she could make out what was being said.

"Who picked my rapunzel? Was it you, woman?"

She turned about and stood up quickly. There, in front of the woman, was the strangest looking person she had ever seen. "Sure this is a woman," she thought, "but how small and how different from any other woman."

Indeed the woman who stood there would have come just up to the waist of any grown-up. And she wore a dress of black cloth and gloves of black cloth and a pointy hat of black cloth. Her face, as much of it could be seen under the hat, had features the likes of which one can hardly imagine. Her nose was narrow and pointed, but at the tip it curved downward toward its owner's mouth, and the ears also ended in points, and hanging from each ear was a big golden earring.

Finally, the housewife managed to say something: "Yes, oh yes, it was I who picked the rapunzel. I'm sorry I did, but I didn't know you had planted it. I found it growing right in my garden, near my lettuce."

"What makes you think this is your garden? I had this garden a long time before you and your husband built your house here. I have lived here for many hundreds of years."

The housewife could hardly believe her ears—hundreds of years? How is that possible?

"Who are you, please?" she said, scarcely able to keep herself from trembling at what she had heard from the strange woman of the forest.

"It is not for you to know who I am. Just understand that I also live here—I will not tell you just where—and I come by when I wish, and I plant the rapunzel and I eat the rapunzel. And you must eat it no more."

"I promise," said the housewife.

"Promises are not enough. Many times in my long life have I heard the likes of you make promises. I will see that you keep your promise."

"How's that?" said the housewife. "How do you mean?"

"I know that you and your husband do not have a child. I also know that both of you have always wanted one. So, to make certain you will not pick the rapunzel again, I will see to it that you will have a child. That child will be yours to keep only as long as you keep out of my bed of rapunzel. If you ever pick it again, you will find

that I have taken your child away and you will never see the child again."

The housewife stared in amazement and fear.

"Furthermore, when your child is born, it will be a girl, and you will call her Rapunzel. That will make certain that you never forget where she came from and what your promise means."

In a moment the little woman of the forest was gone. The housewife didn't even see her go.

Later that evening, after the husband returned from his work, his wife told him what had happened that afternoon. He listened carefully and then said, "I don't know who that woman is, but if what she said was true, then we must make certain we never break your promise."

Sure enough, months later, a baby was born in the house on the edge of the forest, and her father and mother named her Rapunzel. She was a beautiful baby, with fine golden wisps of hair that made her parents glow with pride every time they looked at her.

To prevent Rapunzel from picking any of the forbidden plants from the garden bed, which grew there every summer along with the lettuce and other vegetables, she was never permitted to play outside without having one of her parents nearby. Instead, Rapunzel played mainly in her little room at the top of the house. She was happy enough to play there, since there were no children to play with. She had dolls and games and books to occupy herself with. And, of course, as she grew older, she helped her mother in the kitchen and with other household chores. And so the years went by.

Finally, when Rapunzel had grown up quite a bit,

she drew near the age when she imagined—like the girls in the books she read—that she would one day marry. She read of handsome young princes and strong fishermen and bold soldiers and wondered who her husband would be.

She sometimes would sit in front of her window, with the sun streaming in, and brush her long golden hair until it would shine in the sun. Her mother had never cut Rapunzel's hair. Instead, each night while Rapunzel was a child, her mother had braided the girl's hair just before bedtime. Now Rapunzel was old enough to do the braiding herself, and each night—singing softly to herself— this was her last chore before saying her prayers and getting into bed.

Rapunzel's braids were so long that she had to wear them in a tight coil about her head, but Rapunzel did not care. She was pleased that her hair was so long and so golden.

One evening, while Rapunzel was braiding her hair and singing to herself, she heard a voice that seemed to come from the garden. She looked out her window and there—though it was not easy to see in the gathering dusk—was the little old woman. Rapunzel had never heard of her but thought the woman looked somehow familiar.

"Rapunzel, Rapunzel,
Let down your hair."

Rapunzel undid her braids and let her hair fall down the side of the house. It was long enough to reach almost to the ground, and the little woman quickly climbed up the golden hair and entered Rapunzel's room.

"You don't know who I am, but I wanted to have a close look at you. I have watched you many times while you were combing and braiding your hair. I think you are the most beautiful young woman I have ever seen, and I know you will be going out in the world soon."

"Thank you," said Rapunzel. "I am pleased that you think so. Would you please tell me who you are and where you live."

"That is not for you to know, but if you tell your parents we have met, they will explain everything to you."

With that, the little woman vanished. She, of course, was the same woman who had planted the forbidden rapunzel so many years before.

Rapunzel quickly braided her hair and went downstairs to tell her parents what had happened.

Rapunzel didn't have to say much before her parents knew just what had happened and who the visitor had been. They also knew that their daughter would soon be going out into the world.

Sure enough, no sooner than Rapunzel went back to her room, she heard once more:

"Rapunzel, Rapunzel,
Let down your hair."

She went to the window, and there beneath her, his face catching light from the kitchen below, stood a young man.

Rapunzel once more undid her braids and let her golden hair fall in a long strand from her window toward the ground below. The handsome young man climbed quickly up to Rapunzel's window. When he came into the room, he said to Rapunzel, "I heard the little old woman call to you, and when I saw your face at the window and your golden hair let down nearly to the ground, I knew that I must see you and speak with you."

And speak they did, for more than an hour. The young man turned out to be the son of the King whose lands stretched far and wide, taking in the entire forest and many fine castles. Soon he declared his love for her. Needless to say, Rapunzel felt the same love for the Prince, and the two of them went downstairs to where Rapunzel's parents sat. They had heard all the words that had passed between the two young people and quickly gave their consent to marriage of the young couple.

In a few minutes Rapunzel had packed up her few things and gone off with the Prince, sitting with him on his horse. Rapunzel and her Prince were married in the King's finest castle and lived happily ever after.

The Hare and the Tortoise

AESOP

A YOUNG HARE was skipping about happily one day, now and then taking leaps through the air, and thinking he must be the springiest animal in the fields.

Just as he landed after a big leap, he found himself standing next to a young tortoise.

"Hello there, my friend tortoise," said the hare. "I see you're digesting your lunch."

"That's right," said the tortoise. "How are you to-day?"

"Fine, just fine," said the hare. "Full of good spirits and enjoying the sunshine. "Say, tortoise, how about a race? Nothing like a good race."

The tortoise began to laugh. "Come now, my friend, why would a tortoise race a hare? I've got this big shell to carry around with me. I'm not made for racing hares."

"I'll give you a head start, friend tortoise. See that elm tree over there? I'll give you a one-hour start. I'll get the old donkey to be the judge. How about it, slowpoke?"

Well, thought the tortoise, I'm not going to sit still when someone calls me slowpoke. "All right. Let's do it."

The tortoise started off in his slow, steady way. What did the hare do? He lay down on his back, and soon enough the heat of day made him fall asleep.

By the time the hare woke up, the tortoise was two steps away from the elm tree. And try as hard as the hare could, the tortoise won the race.

THE RACE IS NOT ALWAYS TO THE SWIFT.

Alice Meets Humpty Dumpty

LEWIS CARROLL

THE EGG GOT LARGER and larger, and more and more human. When she had come within a few yards of it, she saw that it had eyes and a nose and mouth. And when she had come close to it, she saw clearly that it was Humpty Dumpty himself. "It can't be anybody else!" she said to herself. "I'm as certain of it as if his name were written all over his face."

Humpty Dumpty was sitting with his legs crossed, like a Turk, on the top of a high wall—such a narrow one that Alice quite wondered how he could keep his balance—and, as his eyes were steadily fixed in the

75

opposite direction, and he didn't take the least notice of her, she thought he must be a stuffed figure after all.

"And how exactly like an egg he is!" she said aloud, standing with her hands ready to catch him, for she was every moment expecting him to fall.

"It's *very* provoking," Humpty Dumpty said after a long silence, looking away from Alice as he spoke, "to be called an egg—*very!*"

"I said you *looked* like an egg, Sir," Alice gently explained. "And some eggs are very pretty, you know," she added, hoping to turn her remark into a sort of compliment.

"Some people," said Humpty Dumpty, looking away from her as usual, "have no more sense than a baby!"

Alice didn't know what to say to this. It wasn't at all like conversation, she thought, as he never said

anything to *her*. In fact, his last remark was evidently addressed to a tree—so she stood and softly repeated to herself:

Humpty Dumpty sat on a wall:
Humpty Dumpty had a great fall.
All the King's horses and all the King's men
Couldn't put Humpty Dumpty in his place again.

"That last line is much too long for the poetry," she added, almost out loud, forgetting that Humpty Dumpty would hear her.

"Don't stand chattering to yourself like that," Humpty Dumpty said, looking at her for the first time, "but tell me your name and your business."

"My *name* is Alice, but —"

"It's a stupid name enough!" Humpty Dumpty interrupted impatiently. "What does it mean?"

"Must a name mean something?" Alice asked.

"Of course it must," Humpty Dumpty said with a short laugh. "*My* name means the shape I am—and a good handsome shape it is, too. With a name like yours, you might be any shape, almost."

"Why do you sit out here all alone?" said Alice, not wishing to begin an argument.

"Why, because there's nobody with me!" cried Humpty Dumpty. "Did you think I didn't know the answer to *that*? Ask another."

"Don't you think you'd be safer down on the ground?" Alice went on, not with any idea of making another riddle, but simply in her good-natured anxiety for the queer creature. "That wall is so very narrow!"

"What tremendously easy riddles you ask!" Humpty Dumpty growled out. "Of course I don't think so! Why, if ever I *did* fall off—which there's no chance of—but *if* I did—" Here he pursed up his lips and looked so solemn and grand that Alice could hardly help laughing. "*If* I did fall," he went on, "the King has promised me—ah, you may turn pale, if you like! The King has promised me, with his very own mouth, to—"

"To send all his horses and all his men," Alice interrupted, rather unwisely.

"Now I declare that's too bad!" Humpty Dumpty cried, breaking into a sudden passion. "You've been listening at doors, and behind trees, and down chimneys, or you couldn't have known it!"

"I haven't, indeed!" Alice said very gently. "It's in a book."

"Ah, well! They may write such things in a *book*," Humpty Dumpty said in a calmer tone. "That's what you call a History of England, that is. Now, take a good look at me! I'm one that has spoken to a King, *I* am.

Mayhap you'll never see such another, and to show you I'm not proud, you may shake hands with me!" And he grinned almost from ear to ear, as he leant forwards (and as nearly as possible fell off the wall in doing so) and offered Alice his hand.

She watched him a little anxiously as she took it. "If he smiled much more, the ends of his mouth might meet behind," she thought, "and then I don't know what would happen to his head! I'm afraid it would come off!"

"Yes, all his horses and all his men," Humpty Dumpty went on. "They'd pick me up again in a minute, they would! However, this conversation is going on a little too fast. Let's go back to the last remark but one."

"I'm afraid I can't quite remember it," Alice said very politely.

"In that case we start fresh," said Humpty Dumpty, "and it's my turn to choose a subject." ("He talks about it just as if it was a game!" thought Alice.) "So here's a question for you. How old did you say you were?"

Alice made a short calculation, and said "Seven years and six months."

"Wrong!" Humpty Dumpty exclaimed triumphantly. "You never said a word like it!"

"I thought you meant 'How old are you?'" Alice explained.

"If I'd meant that, I'd have said it," said Humpty Dumpty.

Alice didn't want to begin another argument, so she said nothing.

"Seven years and six months!" Humpty Dumpty repeated thoughtfully. "An uncomfortable sort of age. Now if you'd asked *my* advice, I'd have said 'Leave off at seven'—but it's too late now."

"I never ask advice about growing," Alice said indignantly.

"Too proud?" the other enquired.

Alice felt even more indignant at this suggestion. "I mean," she said, "that one can't help growing older."

"*One* can't, perhaps," said Humpty Dumpty, "but *two* can. With proper assistance, you might have left off at seven."

"What a beautiful belt you've got on!" Alice suddenly remarked. (They had had quite enough of the subject of age, she thought, and if they really were to take turns in choosing subjects, it was her turn now.) "At least," she corrected herself on second thoughts, "a beautiful cravat, I should have said—no, a belt, I mean—I beg your pardon!" she added in dismay, for Humpty Dumpty looked thoroughly offended, and she began to wish she hadn't chosen that subject. "If only I knew," she thought to herself, "which was neck and which was waist!"

Evidently Humpty Dumpty was very angry, though he said nothing for a minute or two. When he *did* speak again, it was in a deep growl.

"It is a most provoking thing," he said at last, "when a person doesn't know a cravat from a belt!"

"I know it's very ignorant of me," Alice said, in so humble a tone that Humpty Dumpty relented.

"It's a cravat, child, and a beautiful one, as you say. It's a present from the White King and Queen!"

"Is it really?" said Alice, quite pleased to find that she *had* chosen a good subject, after all.

"They gave it me," Humpty Dumpty continued thoughtfully, as he crossed one knee over the other and clasped his hands round it, "they gave it me—for an un-birthday present."

"I beg your pardon?" Alice said with a puzzled air.

"I'm not offended," said Humpty Dumpty.

"I mean, what *is* an un-birthday present?"

"A present given when it isn't your birthday, of course," Humpty Dumpty answered.

Alice considered a little. "I like birthday presents best," she said at last.

"You don't know what your're talking about!" cried Humpty Dumpty. "How many days are there in a year?"

"Three hundred and sixty-five," said Alice.

"And how many birthdays have you?"

"One."

"And if you take one from three hundred and sixty-five, what remains?"

"Three hundred and sixty-four, of course."

Humpty Dumpty looked doubtful. "I'd rather see that done on paper," he said.

Alice couldn't help smiling as she took out her memorandum-book, and worked the sum for him:

$$\begin{array}{r} 365 \\ \underline{1} \\ 364 \end{array}$$

Humpty Dumpty took the book, and looked at it carefully. "That seems to be done right," he began.

"You're holding it upside down!" Alice interrupted.

"To be sure I was!" Humpty Dumpty said gaily, as she turned it round for him. "I thought it looked a little queer. As I was saying, that *seems* to be done right—though I haven't time to look it over thoroughly just now—and that shows that there are three hundred and sixty-four days when you might get un-birthday presents. And only *one* for birthday presents, you know!"

The Cat
and the Pain-Killer

MARK TWAIN

The Adventures of Tom Sawyer *tells the story of a boy who grew up in a small town on the Mississippi River about 100 years ago. Tom and his friends really did have adventures — they got lost in a cave, they were witnesses in a murder trial, and one time they even disappeared on an island in the river. During all this, Tom lived with his Aunt Polly who, at times, found Tom's shenanigans more than she could handle.*

TOM'S MIND HAD DRIFTED away from its secret troubles. It had found a new and weighty matter to interest itself about. Becky Thatcher had stopped coming to school. Tom had struggled with his pride a few days, and tried to "whistle her down the wind," but failed. He began to find himself hanging around her father's house, nights, and feeling very miserable. She was ill. What if she should die? There was distraction in the thought. He no longer took an interest in war, nor even in piracy. He put his hoop away and his bat; there was no joy in them any more. His aunt was concerned.

She began to try all manner of remedies on him. She was one of those people who are infatuated with patent medicines and all new-fangled methods of producing

health or mending it. She was an inveterate experimenter in these things. When something fresh in this line came out she was in a fever, right away, to try it—not on herself, for she was never ailing, but on anybody else that came handy. She was a subscriber for all the "Health" periodicals. The solemn ignorance they were inflated with was breath to her nostrils. She never observed that her health journals of the current month customarily upset everything they had recommended the month before. She was as simple-hearted and honest as the day is long and so she was an easy victim.

The water treatment was new now, and Tom's low condition was a windfall to her. She had him out at daylight every morning, stood him up in the woodshed and drowned him with a deluge of cold water. Then she scrubbed him down with a towel like a file, and so brought him to. Then she rolled him up in a wet sheet and put him away under blankets till she sweated his soul clean and "the yellow stains of it came through his pores"—as Tom said.

Yet notwithstanding all this, the boy grew more and more melancholy and pale and dejected. She added hot baths, sitz baths, shower baths, and plunges. The boy remained as dismal as a hearse. She began to assist the water with a slim oatmeal diet and blister-plasters. She calculated his capacity as she would a jug's, and filled him up every day with quack cure-alls.

Tom had become indifferent to persecution by this time. This phase filled the old lady's heart with consternation. This indifference must be broken up at any cost. Now she heard of Pain-killer for the first time. She ordered a lot at once. She tasted it and was filled with gratitude. It was simply fire in a liquid form. She dropped the water treatment and everything else, and pinned her faith to Pain-killer. She gave Tom a teaspoonful and watched with the deepest anxiety for the result. Her troubles were instantly at rest, her soul at peace again, for the "indifference" was broken up. The boy could not have shown a wilder, heartier interest if she had built a fire under him.

Tom felt that it was time to wake up. This sort of life might be romantic enough, in his blighted condition, but it was getting to have too little sentiment and too much distracting variety about it. So he thought over various plans for relief, and finally hit upon that of professing to be fond of Pain-killer. He asked for it so often that he became a nuisance, and his aunt ended by telling him to help himself and quit bothering her. If it had been Sid, she would have had no misgivings to alloy her delight; but since it was Tom, she watched the bottle clandestinely. She found that the medicine did really diminish, but it did not occur to her that the boy was mending the health of a crack in the sitting-room floor with it.

One day Tom was in the act of dosing the crack when his aunt's yellow cat came along, purring, eyeing the teaspoon avariciously, and begging for a taste. Tom said: "Don't ask for it unless you want it, Peter."

But Peter signified that he did want it.

"You better make sure."

Peter was sure.

"Now you've asked for it, and I'll give it to you, because there ain't anything mean about *me*. But if you find you don't like it, you mustn't blame anybody but your own self."

Peter was agreeable. So Tom pried his mouth open and poured down the Pain-killer. Peter sprang a couple of yards in the air, and then delivered a war-whoop and set off round and round the room, banging against furniture, upsetting flower pots, and making general havoc. Next he rose on his hind feet and pranced around, in a

frenzy of enjoyment, with his head over his shoulder and his voice proclaiming his unappeasable happiness. Then he went tearing around the house again, spreading chaos and destruction in his path. Aunt Polly entered in time to see him throw a few double somersaults, deliver a final mighty hurrah, and sail through the open window, carrying the rest of the flower pots with him. The old lady stood petrified with astonishment, peering over her glasses. Tom lay on the floor expiring with laughter.

"Tom, what on earth ails that cat?"

"*I* don't know, aunt," gasped the boy.

"Why, I never see anything like it. What *did* make him act so?"

"'Deed I don't know, Aunt Polly. Cats always act so when they're having a good time."

"They do, do they?" There was something in the tone that made Tom apprehensive.

"Yes'm. That is, I believe they do."

"You *do?*"

"Yes'm!"

The old lady was bending down, Tom watching, with interest emphasized by anxiety. Too late he divined her drift. The handle of the telltale teaspoon was visible under the bed valance. Aunt Polly took it, held it up. Tom winced, and dropped his eyes. Aunt Polly raised him by the usual handle—his ear—and cracked his head soundly with her thimble.

"Now, sir, what did you want to treat that poor dumb beast so for?"

"I done it out of pity for him—because he hadn't any aunt."

"Hadn't any aunt!—you numskull. What has that got to do with it?"

"Heaps. Because if he'd 'a' had one she'd 'a' burnt him out herself! She'd 'a' roasted his bowels out of him 'thout any more feeling than if he was a human!"

Aunt Polly felt a sudden pang of remorse. This was putting the thing in a new light. What was cruelty to a cat *might* be cruelty to a boy, too. She began to soften; she felt sorry. Her eyes watered a little, and she put her hand on Tom's head and said gently:

"I was meaning for the best, Tom. And, Tom, it *did* do you good."

Tom looked up in her face with just a perceptible twinkle peeping through his gravity.

"I know you was meaning for the best, auntie, and so was I with Peter. It done *him* good, too. I never see him get around so since—"

"Oh, go 'long with you, Tom, before you aggravate me again. And you try and see if you can't be a good boy, for once, and you needn't take any more medicine.

Wynken, Blynken, and Nod one night
   Sailed off in a wooden shoe—
Sailed on a river of crystal light,
   Into a sea of dew.
"Where are you going, and what do you wish?"
   The old moon asked the three.
"We have come to fish for the herring fish
   That live in this beautiful sea;
   Nets of silver and gold have we!"
         Said Wynken,
         Blynken,
         And Nod.

Wynken, Blynken, and Nod

The old moon laughed and sang a song,
   As they rocked in the wooden shoe,
And the wind that sped them all night long
   Ruffled the waves of dew.
The little stars were the herring fish
   That lived in that beautiful sea—
"Now cast your nets wherever you wish—
   Never afeard are we";
   So cried the stars to the fishermen three:
         Wynken,
         Blynken,
         And Nod.

All night long their nets they threw
　　To the stars in the twinkling foam—
Then down from the skies came the wooden shoe,
　　Bringing the fishermen home;
'Twas all so pretty a sail it seemed
　　As if it could not be,
And some folks thought 'twas a dream they'd dreamed
　　Of sailing that beautiful sea—
　　But I shall name you the fishermen three:
　　　　　　Wynken,
　　　　　　Blynken,
　　　　　　And Nod.

Wynken and Blynken are two little eyes,
　　And Nod is a little head,
And the wooden shoe that sailed the skies
　　Is a wee one's trundle-bed.
So shut your eyes while mother sings
　　Of wonderful sights that be,
And you shall see the beautiful things
　　As you rock in the misty sea,
　　Where the old shoe rocked the fishermen three:
　　　　　　Wynken,
　　　　　　Blynken,
　　　　　　And Nod.

EUGENE FIELD

Barbara Frietchie

Up from the meadows rich with corn,
Clear in the cool September morn,

The clustered spires of Frederick stand
Green-walled by the hills of Maryland.

Round about them orchards sweep,
Apple and peach tree fruited deep,

Fair as the garden of the Lord
To the eyes of the famished rebel horde,

On that pleasant morn of the early fall
When Lee marched over the mountain wall;

Over the mountains winding down,
Horse and foot, into Frederick town.

Up rose old Barbara Frietchie then,
Bowed with her fourscore years and ten;

Bravest of all in Frederick town,
She took up the flag the men hauled down;

In her attic window the staff she set,
To show that one heart was loyal yet.

Up the street came the rebel tread,
Stonewall Jackson riding ahead.

Under his slouched hat left and right
He glanced; the old flag met his sight.

"Halt!"—the dust-brown ranks stood fast,
"Fire!"—out blazed the rifle-blast.

It shivered the window, pane and sash;
It rent the banner with seam and gash.

Quick as it fell, from the broken staff
Dame Barbara snatched the silken scarf.

She leaned far out on the window-sill,
And shook it forth with a royal will.

"Shoot, if you must, this old gray head,
But spare your country's flag," she said.

A shade of sadness, a blush of shame,
Over the face of the leader came;

The nobler nature within him stirred
To life at that woman's deed and word;

"Who touches a hair of yon gray head
Dies like a dog! March on!" he said.

All day long through Frederick street
Sounded the tread of marching feet:

All day long that free flag tossed
Over the heads of the rebel host.

Barbara Frietchie's work is o'er,
And the Rebel rides on his raids no more.

Over Barbara Frietchie's grave,
Flag of Freedom and Union, wave!

And ever the stars above look down
On thy stars below in Frederick town!

JOHN GREENLEAF WHITTIER

Holidays and Entertainments

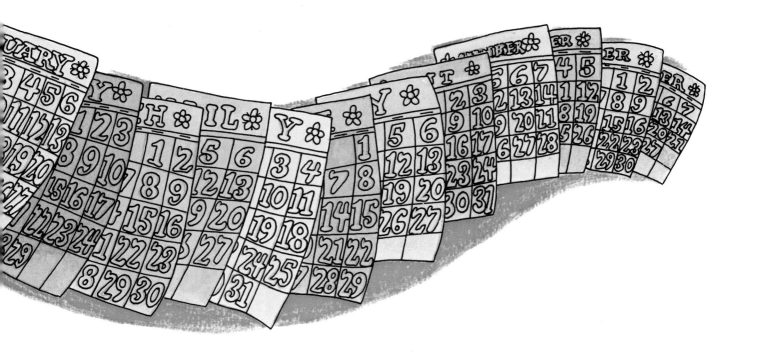

American Holidays

New Year's Day

THE CLOCK IS ABOUT TO STRIKE midnight. It is New Year's Eve. In New York hundreds of thousands of people have jammed into Times Square—the center of the city—to welcome the new year. The last seconds of the old year tick away. When 12 o'clock arrives, a great cheer goes up, horns blow, firecrackers explode, and people sing "Should old acquaintance be forgot, and days of auld lang syne." It is now January 1st, the beginning of a new year.

New Year's Day is the world's birthday. It is celebrated in almost every country in the world. It is a day to look back over the past year and remember all the good things that have happened. It is a time to look back at mistakes, and to make "resolutions" to avoid these mistakes in the new year.

People celebrate New Year's Day in different ways throughout the world. In England and Scotland, large bonfires are built. In France, gifts are exchanged on New Year's Day. In some countries children go from door to door to receive cookies and cakes.

Perhaps the most popular custom throughout the world is going visiting. People in many parts of the world open their doors to greet their friends and neighbors on New Year's Day. Cookies, candies, nuts, cakes, and other good things are offered at each house. This friendly custom began in China many years ago.

There have been some strange customs on New Year's Day. They are *superstitions*. That is, they are strange ideas people believed even though there was no real reason to believe them. That a rabbit's foot brings good luck or that breaking a mirror brings seven years bad luck are superstitions.

The most famous superstition for New Year's Day is called "first footing." People in many European countries believed that the first visitor who entered their house on New Year's Day would bring either good luck or bad luck for the whole year. A dark-haired man would bring good luck. A woman or a man with light hair would bring bad luck. So, to be on the safe side, some towns chose a man with dark hair to go quickly from house to house. After he made his rounds, the houses would be open to other visitors.

In Japan, women placed beans on the floor in the four corners of the house. This was supposed to drive evil spirits from the house for the new year.

In the United States the new year is celebrated with New Year's Eve parties, paper hats, noise, music, and good friendship. Parades are also an important part of the celebration.

The "Mummers" parade on January 1st each year in Philadelphia, Pennsylvania, is one of the biggest parades in the world. A "mummer" is a man who wears a mask or costume. The Philadelphia parade lasts 10 hours, and is said to cost over one million dollars. The leader of the parade is called "King Momus," and is dressed in a brightly colored costume. He is followed by a long line of magnificent floats, each one different, and specially decorated for the occasion. There are marching bands. The men in the parade

are dressed as clowns, animals, historical figures, and even women (because no women are allowed in the parade). The costumes are gay and colorful, and many are covered with flowers, baubles, sequins, and jewelry.

On the other coast of the United States in Pasadena, California, is another famous parade — the Tournament of Roses. A "queen" leads the parade. Millions of flowers, especially roses, decorate the floats. It is one of the most beautiful parades in the world. The climax of the pageant is the Rose Bowl football game.

Everyone, however, does not celebrate the new year on January 1st. The date of the new year depends on the calendar that is used. In the past, different days have been New Year's Day because of the different calendars that were used. Even today, some countries or groups of people celebrate according to other calendars.

The wonderful thing about New Year's — whenever it occurs — is that a whole new year lies ahead. The sad thing is that another year has passed.

Lincoln's Birthday

ABRAHAM LINCOLN WAS BORN February 12, 1809. He became the 16th president of the United States, and one of the most famous men in our history. Each year we honor the birthday of this great man.

In the woods of Kentucky where Abraham Lincoln was born, the people were very poor. The men were farmers or tradesmen who worked long and hard each day to earn enough to support their families. The

Lincoln family was no different. Abraham was born in a small log cabin. His parents could not read or write. There were no schools nearby. Abraham Lincoln spent at most only one year in school, but he learned to read and write.

The Lincoln family moved to Indiana, and later to Illinois. As a young man, Abraham left home to live in New Salem, Illinois. He worked at various odd jobs, and studied in his spare time. Finally, he entered politics and was elected to the Illinois state assembly. He continued to study. In time he became a lawyer.

He was elected to the United States Congress, but served only one two-year term. He later tried for the Senate. His opponent was Senator Stephen Douglas. Lincoln lost that election, but two years later, in 1860, he ran again against Douglas. This time the two men were running for the presidency of the United States. This time Lincoln won the election.

Shortly after his election, the Civil War broke out. Abraham Lincoln found himself as president in the most difficult years our nation has ever faced.

In 1863, Lincoln bravely met the problem of slavery. He issued the Emancipation Proclamation which freed the slaves in Confederate-held territory.

The Civil War still raged. Abraham Lincoln struggled to bring the nation back together. After four bitter years of fighting, the war ended on April 9, 1865. The United States was again united as one nation.

Five days later, Abraham Lincoln went with his wife to Ford's Theater in Washington, D.C., to watch a play. There he was shot to death by John Wilkes Booth.

The world would not forget this great man. He is remembered each year on February 12th for preserving the country in its most tragic hours. He is honored for the strength and courage he displayed in defending the rights of all men as equal. And he is admired for the wonderful example he left to us of rising through hard work, determination, and skill to the highest office in the United States.

Washington's Birthday

WASHINGTON, D.C., the state of Washington, the Washington Monument, the George Washington Bridge —almost everywhere in the United States there is something named after George Washington. He is America's most famous leader, called the "Father of His Country."

It is only proper that we honor Washington's birthday as a holiday. George Washington was a great general who led our army against the British in our war of independence, the Revolutionary War. He defeated the British forces, and America became a new, free nation.

After the war, in 1789, George Washington was elected the first president of the United States. He served for eight years. Washington helped to establish our Constitution, and helped build a new and orderly government. He provided the foundation so the United States could grow into a great nation.

Washington's birthday is celebrated on the third Monday in February. He was born February 11, 1732. The

calendar was changed 20 years later and his birthday became February 22. Unlike Abraham Lincoln, George Washington was born of fairly wealthy parents in Virginia. At 16, he went to live at Mount Vernon, a beautiful home on the Potomac River in Alexandria, Virginia. This was to be his home for the rest of his life. It is there that Washington is buried. Today, Mount Vernon is one of the most famous landmarks in the United States.

The first celebration of Washington's birthday was in 1781. It was a great honor, because Washington was still alive. Troops marched in the streets, and the day was made a holiday. Very few men in history have received such an honor in their lifetime.

Today, Washington's birthday is celebrated with cherry pies and talk of little boys chopping down cherry trees. In schools throughout the United States, children read and write stories about his wonderful deeds.

George Washington did not chop down a cherry tree and then confess the misdeed to his father. That was only a story made up years after his death to show that he was a brave and honest man. No stories are necessary, however, to show the greatness of George Washington. His devotion and courage led an army through Valley Forge and to victory in the Revolution. His honesty and loyalty helped to establish our nation.

Easter

EASTER COMES IN THE SPRING each year. It is a joyful celebration because it honors the resurrection of Christ. It is the day he is said to have risen from the dead. This happy day follows a long period of penance and mourning for the death of Jesus Christ. The 40 days, called *Lent*, begin on Ash Wednesday. They extend through Good Friday, the day of Christ's crucifixion, and end on Easter Sunday.

Easter occurs on a different Sunday each year. It is celebrated on the first Sunday that follows the first full moon after March 21st (the first day of spring). The Roman Emperor Constantine, who was a Christian, set this date for Easter back in the year 325 A.D. Most churches have followed his rule ever since.

The celebration of Easter is one of the most important holidays in Christian countries throughout the world. But many Easter customs are not religious. In America, there is an Easter "parade." In towns and cities, people go walking in their newest clothes. Men sometimes dress formally, even to a high silk hat. And women and girls must have a new Easter bonnet.

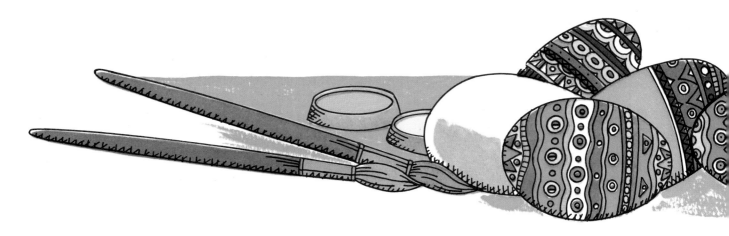

Brightly colored Easter eggs are another part of the celebration. In some areas they are given out on Easter morning. In other places, they are hidden, and children must hunt for them. Egg-rolling is another Easter pastime. Each year, an egg-rolling contest is held on the lawn of the White House in Washington. Contests are also held in England and Germany.

How did eggs come to be part of the Easter celebration? Perhaps because they are the symbol of new life. Christ's resurrection was a new life. Also, Easter comes at the beginning of spring, when all of nature comes to life after the cold winter.

The Easter rabbit appears each year, too. In Germany, people say the Easter rabbit brings the eggs and hides them in houses. This idea was brought over to the United States by German settlers.

In Russia and many of the other Slavic countries, Easter eggs are works of art. Beautiful and intricate designs of many colors are drawn on the eggs. They are painted by hand, and many are saved and passed down through the generations. The custom also includes taking the eggs to church to be blessed. In Italy, also, eggs are taken to church to be blessed.

Easter eggs, parades, and bunnies have no part at all in the Latin American Easter. All of Holy Week — the week before Easter — is a religious festival in Mexico

and South America. On Palm Sunday, palm leaves are blessed in the churches, as they are in many North American churches. Churches are decorated with fruit and green plants. There are religious processions and *passion plays,* telling the Easter story.

People go into deep mourning on Good Friday, but Catholics in Latin America celebrate the resurrection on Easter Saturday. After church, people go into a wild celebration, with whistles, church bells, and fireworks! In many places, people play rough games with a straw figure dressed up as Judas, who told the Roman soldiers where to capture Jesus. The Judas is hanged or burned by the crowd.

In Europe, too, there are many solemn processions on Good Friday. These are sad funeral processions mourning the death of Christ. In a town in Italy, young men run through the streets. As they run, they hit themselves on the legs with pieces of cork studded with broken glass, so that they will be hurt as Christ was.

Lent, the 40 days of penance, is an important and serious part of the Easter season. And *Carnival,* right before Lent, is the wildest holiday of the year in many parts of Europe and Latin America. There are great parades, street dances, and costume balls for three days or even longer. The biggest South American carnival is in Rio de Janeiro, Brazil. Even the very poorest people work for months to have a beautiful costume for the street dances.

French settlers brought this custom of carnival over to the United States. A *Mardi Gras* carnival is held in New Orleans each year.

Mardi Gras really means "Fat Tuesday" in French, because everyone tries to eat up the good things they will not eat after Lent begins on Ash Wednesday. In England, people often have pancake festivals. In Germany, they make doughnuts.

With all the parades and customs, though, Easter is still mainly a time to celebrate new life. Spring is in the air. The long days of winter and of Lent are over. It is a day to remember the man who was born on Christmas, died on Good Friday, and rose again on Easter Sunday.

Memorial Day

MEMORIAL DAY is the one holiday each year that is not a happy celebration. It is a special day for honoring those Americans who have died defending their country. The last Monday in May is devoted to their memory.

The United States has been through many wars—the Revolutionary War, the War of 1812, the Civil War, World Wars I and II, Korea, Vietnam. Hundreds of thousands of Americans have died on battlefields all over the world. The memory of their great sacrifice is kept alive each Memorial Day.

The custom began one year after the end of the Civil War. A group of women in Mississippi decided

to honor the graves of both Northern and Southern soldiers who had died at the battle of Shiloh in the Civil War. They decorated the graves with flowers. Two years later, in 1868, Gen. John A. Logan, commander of the Grand Army of the Republic, set aside a special day to honor those fallen in battle.

Because people placed flowers on the soldiers' graves, the day became known as Decoration Day. Even today in many parts of the United States, Memorial Day is called Decoration Day.

Today, people observe Memorial Day in much the same way as in the past. Flowers are placed on graves, and people pray for the brave men who have died. There are parades, speeches, and memorial services.

At military bases and aboard Navy ships, the flag is flown at half-mast. At noon, a memorial service is held. An honor guard stands at rigid attention while memorial services are said. A 21-gun salute and the sad notes of "Taps" played by a bugler end the ceremony.

In many ports of the United States, tiny boats filled with flowers are set afloat. From U.S. Navy ships, flowers are thrown overboard to float on the sea. These customs are to honor those who have died at sea.

At the Tomb of the Unknowns—formerly called The Tomb of the Unknown Soldier—near Washington, D.C., a ceremony is held. Buried in this tomb are men killed in all the great wars since World War I. No one knows who these men were. All that is known is that they died for their country. The tomb stands to remind all Americans of the brave men who have died in battle.

Independence Day

IN THE HOT SUMMER of 1776, more than fifty men were gathered at a meeting place in Philadelphia. They were considering a document carefully written by Thomas Jefferson. It was the Declaration of Independence, the colonies' demand for their freedom.

The Revolutionary War had already begun. Paul Revere had made his famous ride to warn about the approaching British soldiers. The Minutemen had fought bravely at Concord and Lexington in Massachusetts. George Washington had been given command of the American armies fighting against the British. And Thomas Paine had called for independence and freedom in his famous essay, *Common Sense*.

The 56 men in Philadelphia represented all thirteen colonies. Such famous patriots as Benjamin Franklin, John Adams, and John Hancock were among them.

On July 4, 1776, the final version of the declaration was approved. The thirteen British colonies in America became the United States of America. All ties with England were broken. A new nation was born.

The War of Independence continued, but now there was a real cause to fight for. The cries were *liberty, freedom, independence.* Finally, in 1781, after Washington defeated Lord Cornwallis at Yorktown, Virginia, the British admitted defeat.

The first celebration of Independence Day was held in 1777, the year after the signing of the Declaration of Independence. John Adams predicted that it would be celebrated every year by all generations of Americans to follow. And he was right.

Over the years, Independence Day has been celebrated with firecrackers, sparklers, skyrockets, and roman candles. Because fireworks are dangerous, most states in the United States today restrict their use to outside displays that are carefully supervised.

Parades, marching bands, and picnics are other parts of the Fourth of July celebration. Homes display the American flag. And cities and towns are decorated with red, white, and blue bunting.

July 4th, Independence Day, is the birthday of the United States. It is a proud and important holiday. And it is a day on which we should be thankful for the wonderful freedoms demanded in the Declaration of Independence, and guaranteed by the Constitution.

Labor Day

IN 1882, A MAN NAMED Peter J. McGuire decided that there should be a holiday to honor the working-man. There were holidays, he said, to remember important patriotic, religious, and military persons. But what about the important people who work hard every day of the year? They, too, should be honored.

Peter McGuire suggested setting aside the first Monday in September each year as a holiday for the working people. He named it Labor Day. The first Monday in September was chosen because it was a pleasant time of year. Also, there was no holiday between July 4th and Thanksgiving. Most people agreed with him and thought it was a fine idea. So the first Labor Day was celebrated in 1882 in New York City.

The idea of honoring men for the work they did all year long spread quickly. In 1894, President Grover Cleveland signed a law to make the first Monday in September a national holiday.

Life was not always easy for the workingman, even in the United States. In the early 1800's men worked 12 to 15 hours a day. Women and children, too, worked long hours in factories and mines. Jobs were often dangerous. Pay was very little, barely enough for a family to live on. If a man got sick and could not work he was not paid. Some men had to work seven days a week.

After the Civil War, laborers began to organize. They wanted better working conditions and better wages. Men thought they would have a better chance as a group to face their employers. That was the beginning of *labor unions.*

The first labor union was the Knights of Labor, founded by Uriah S. Stephens in 1869. In 1886, Samuel Gompers started the American Federation of Labor (AFL). It became very large and powerful. The AFL gained higher wages and better working conditions for its members. In 1935, the Congress of Industrial Organizations (CIO) was established. In 1955, the AFL and CIO joined together.

Today, there are no longer 12-hour working days. There are good wages. Workers also get insurance, pensions, and pay when they are sick. But more important, workers have gained respect. After all, the United States grew into a great nation by the hard work of many men, who work at their jobs every day of the year.

That is why we celebrate Labor Day.

Halloween

HALLOWEEN IS THE NIGHT for ghosts and goblins, witches and black cats, haunted houses and the rattling bones of skeletons. It is the time, some say, that the headless horseman rides through the streets, his great sword flashing in the night.

Each October 31st, people almost everywhere celebrate Halloween. In the United States, children dress in costumes, They go from house to house, calling "Trick or treat." And woe to the person who cannot find some candy or cookies, an apple, or even a penny for the callers. In some places, bonfires blaze against the sky. People duck for apples. And pumpkins are carved and placed in windows to leer out at people.

Long ago many people really believed in ghosts and witches. To protect themselves and to frighten away the ghosts and witches, they built bonfires. Some wore costumes, some carried torches, and some danced around fires, hoping to scare away the "evil spirits." Many of these customs are part of our Halloween.

In England over 2,000 years ago, the Celts held a ceremony called *Samhain,* which meant "the end of

116

the summer." The Celts believed that at Samhain the ghosts of the dead came back to earth. Bonfires were set ablaze to frighten these ghosts away. The *Druids,* who were priests of the Celts, held strange rituals. They offered human sacrifices to the gods in thanks for the harvest and for protection from the ghosts.

Many years later, the Christians continued some of the customs of Samhain, but they changed it to a different holiday. They set aside November 1st to honor all the saints in the Christian faith. They called the day All Hallows Day or All Saints Day. The evening before was All Hallows Eve, which later was shortened to simply Halloween. They celebrated this evening with bonfires, costumes, and talk of ghosts and witches.

In Ireland, they told a story about poor Jack. He was not allowed to enter heaven because he was too wicked. The devil would not have him either because Jack had played tricks on him. So, Jack was forced to wander over the earth forever, carrying a lantern.

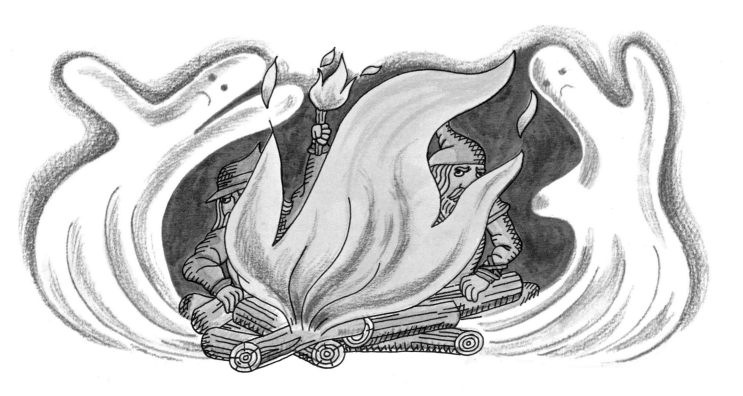

The Irish on Halloween made "jack-o-lanterns" by carving out turnips or potatoes and placing a candle inside. Today, we carve them out of pumpkins.

In England, children beg for "soul-cakes" on Halloween. This custom began a long time ago in England, and was brought to the United States by the English settlers. In America, it was changed to "Trick or treat, money or eat." The children in England beg in different ways. Some say:

Soul! Soul! for a souling-cake!

I pray you, good missus, a souling-cake,

In another part of England, the children call:

Soul! Soul! for an apple or two!

If you have no apples,

Pears will do.

If you have no pears,

Money will do.

If you have no money,

God bless you!

Children in Scotland play a Halloween game. They go out to the fields, close their eyes and pull up a cabbage. The type of cabbage they pull is supposed to determine the kind of person they will marry. A cabbage with a close white head means an old husband. If there is dirt on the roots, the child will marry someone rich. The children then bring the cabbages home and hang them above the door.

Halloween was not celebrated much in the United States until the late 1800's. Today it is one of our favorite holidays. There are Halloween parties with prizes for the best costumes. Treats are given and sometimes tricks are played. Even though there are no ghosts or witches, it is still fun to be frightened on this one night of the year!

Thanksgiving Day

ONE OF THE FIRST really American customs was to set aside one day each year to give thanks. Everyone has something to be thankful for, be it big or small.

The day Americans have set aside to give thanks is the fourth Thursday in November—Thanksgiving Day. It is a day for family gatherings at home. Usually the feast is roast turkey, browned and juicy. There are dressing and gravy, cranberry sauce, potatoes and vegetables. And finally, there is pumpkin pie or mincemeat pie to finish off the meal.

The most important part of Thanksgiving, however, is the giving of thanks for all our blessings. That is the reason this happy holiday was started back in 1621.

The Pilgrims had arrived from England the year before. They had sailed across the ocean on the *Mayflower,* a voyage that took over two months. They had

suffered bitterly through their first winter in the New World, without warm houses or enough food to eat.

When spring came, they planted crops of corn, wheat, barley and vegetables. To get through the next winter, they had to have a good harvest. The Pilgrims worked and prayed. Finally, the harvest was in, and it was very good. The Pilgrims then set aside a day to give thanks to God.

A great feast was planned. The Pilgrims invited friendly Indians from neighboring villages. The feast included wild turkey, lobsters, clams, oysters, and venison (deer meat). The Pilgrims and the Indians feasted for three days. Unfortunately they ate up much of what they had planned to save for the coming winter. When winter came, they were often hungry.

It became the Pilgrims' custom to set aside one day each year for Thanksgiving. They did not, however, make the mistake again of not putting aside enough food to last through the winter.

George Washington called for a national day of Thanksgiving in 1789. It was to give thanks for America's success in the War of Independence. In 1863, President Abraham Lincoln set aside the last Thursday in November to be celebrated each year as Thanksgiving Day.

To observe a day of thanks is not only an American custom. In fact, it goes at least as far back as ancient Greece. The Greeks thousands of years ago had a harvest feast in honor of Demeter, their goddess of farming. The Romans had a feast for their goddess Ceres.

The Jewish people have had days of thanksgiving for thousands of years. The Feast of Tabernacles, or Booths, called *Sukkoth,* is in honor of the harvest. Little booths or baskets were made, and fruits and vegetables placed in them. Then the Jews gave thanks to God.

In many countries today, days of thanksgiving are celebrated. They are usually related to the country's day of independence, and are double celebrations.

In America, we have one day whose only purpose is to give thanks. And we have much to be thankful for.

Christmas

CHRISTMAS IS THE MOST joyful holiday of the year. On that day, December 25th, the birth of Jesus Christ is celebrated.

The birth of Christ so many years ago began a new age—the age of Christianity. His life and teachings have had more effect on the world than those of any other man in history. And on Christmas, his birthday is celebrated in every Christian country in the world.

The story of the first Christmas is perhaps the best known story ever told. Joseph, a carpenter, and his wife Mary had to return to Bethlehem for a census of all Roman citizens. Mary, who was expecting a child, rode upon a donkey. Bethlehem was crowded with

travelers, and there was no lodging to be found. It was a cold winter night. Finally, the wife of an innkeeper allowed Joseph and Mary to stay in a stable behind the inn. There Jesus Christ was born.

That night a great star was seen in the sky. Shepherds in the fields followed the star. It led them to the stable. They found Christ lying in a manger, and fell to their knees to worship the newborn king.

In Persia, three wise men, called the *Magi,* also saw the star and followed it. To them, the star was the signal for the birth of the *Messiah,* come to save the world. It was the first Christmas, quietly and sacredly celebrated in a cold and tiny stable.

Christmas is first a religious holiday. Beautiful ceremonies are held in churches everywhere to honor the birth of Jesus. The churches are decorated, and millions of people attend services.

Christmas is also a day for giving gifts and, of course, receiving them. Santa Claus, that jolly old man from the North Pole, is as much a part of Christmas as fingers are a part of your hand. They say that each Christmas Eve he loads his sleigh with toys, candy, and presents, and delivers them to all good boys and girls.

In some countries gifts are brought by St. Nicholas; in others, by Kris Kringle. The legend of Santa Claus

comes from the story of St. Nicholas, who lived over 1,600 years ago. St. Nicholas is said to have gone from house to house in those days, leaving gifts in the shoes of little children. In Belgium and Holland, it is St. Nicholas who delivers gifts. He brings them on December 6th, his feast day.

The story that Santa Claus comes down the chimney began in Norway many years ago. Our American Santa Claus, with his red suit and white beard, looks like the one in the poem "The Night Before Christmas."

The Christmas tree is another important Christmas custom. With ornaments and lights, tinsel and beads, and, of course, a star or an angel on top, it is a beautiful sight. The Christmas tree first became a part of the celebration in Germany. Some say it began with St. Boniface back in the eighth century. At that time, the Teutons, a tribe of barbarians, would sacrifice a child each year before a great oak tree. St. Boniface suggested that instead of killing a child they should cut down a fir tree, take it home and celebrate around it. Another story is that Martin Luther brought a fir tree home one Christmas Eve in the 1500's. He decorated it with candles to look like the stars in the sky.

Nativity scenes, sometimes called *cribs* or *creches*, show the Baby in the stable, with his family and the

shepherds. Homes and churches throughout the world set up manger scenes. In Bethlehem, Pennsylvania, there is the largest Nativity scene in the world. Hundreds of live animals are used, and people come from miles around to see it. The star placed above it can be seen for twenty miles.

Christmas carols are sung in the streets, in churches, and in homes at Christmas time. Holly, mistletoe, wreaths, and Christmas candles are among the most popular Christmas decorations. And, of course, there is the tradition of hanging a Christmas stocking from the mantel, to be filled by Santa Claus.

These are some ways that Christmas is celebrated in America. But in other parts of the world, there are many other Christmas customs.

In Mexico, the children play a Christmas game. A *piñata,* which is a colorfully decorated jar, is hung from the ceiling. The *piñata* is filled with gifts and candies. One child is blindfolded and given a stick. He swings the stick around in the air. When he hits the *piñata* it breaks, and the presents pour out on the floor. All the children rush to gather up the gifts. A special Mexican Christmas dish is a mixture of fruits and vegetables, covered with all kinds of candies.

The children in France do not hang up Christmas stockings. Instead, they put their shoes outside to be filled with gifts.

In Italy, each child has his own *Ceppo.* A Ceppo is shaped like a Christmas tree, except that it is made with poles and looks like a pyramid. There are shelves where gifts are placed. The bottom shelf is often a nativity scene. The Ceppo is also decorated with candles, ornaments, and pine cones.

The Yule Log is a tradition in many countries. With great ceremony the log is brought in and placed in the fireplace. People in countries as far apart as England and Yugoslavia bring in the Yule Log.

Throughout the world, children go through the streets singing Christmas carols. In Poland, carolers used to carry a star. Many dressed as shepherds and wise men. In some Slavic countries, children receive gifts as they go caroling.

Christmas dinner is always a wonderful event. It, too, is different throughout the world. In America, it is usually turkey or goose. Long ago in England, it was boar's head and brawne, peacock, and mutton pies. Some countries even serve a whole roast pig. In Poland, Christmas dinner has 12 courses. A chair at the table is always left empty in case a traveler stops.

Twelfth Night, January 6th, is an important part of some countries' Christmas celebrations. In England, it was the "twelfth day of Christmas," just as in the song. It was the day to take down the Christmas greens and burn them in a gay celebration. Some people in the United States still follow this custom.

In certain countries, January 6th, called the Day of the Three Kings, is the day of gift-giving. It is believed to be the day that the three wise men, traveling from far countries, finally arrived in Bethlehem to bring the baby Jesus their gifts of gold, frankincense, and myrrh. In Latin America, children get their gifts from the three kings on January 6th, not from Santa Claus. The three kings come riding through town, people say, and leave presents in the children's shoes set outside the door. Thoughtful children, of course, remember to leave hay and water for the kings' camels.

In South America there are exciting parades and fireworks on the Day of the Kings. People dress up as servants from Egypt and Oriental countries to march in the procession ahead of the three kings. Parades in Peru show the three kings as Ethiopian, Inca, and Spanish!

In southern France and in Spain, children go out on the eve of January 6th carrying gifts of fruit and cake for the Christ Child, and hoping to meet the three kings who will deliver their gifts. If they do not see the kings, they take their gifts to the church.

There are many Christmas customs and traditions. And all people have their own special ways of celebrating Christmas. It is a time of great joy. And it should be a time of great charity, a time of giving. After all, it is the day to celebrate the birth of Christ, who gave his life for mankind. Perhaps the best description of Christmas is in the beautiful carol:

> Silent night, Holy night,
> All is calm, all is bright.

Holidays
Throughout the World

Jewish Holidays

THE HOLIDAYS OF THE Jewish people are among the most beautiful celebrations in the world. Jewish holidays are religious, and honor important events in the history of the Jewish people.

The celebrations are held in homes and in the *synagogue,* the house of worship. Ceremonies begin at sunset on the eve of the holiday. These holidays are observed in the Jewish nation, Israel, and by Jewish people throughout the world.

Rosh Hashana is the Jewish New Year. It is a time to repent for past sins and misdeeds. In every synagogue prayers are read. A ram's horn, called a *shofar*, is blown. This is the call for people to remember their past sins and to ask forgiveness for them. At home, the people dip an apple and bread in honey. These acts call for hope in the new year. Rosh Hashana is the first day of a ten-day period of penance.

The tenth day is *Yom Kippur*, one of the holiest of all Jewish holidays. Yom Kippur is the Day of Atonement. It is a day of fasting, when people do not eat or drink. It is another day to repent for all sins. In the synagogue, services begin with the singing of a prayer, the *Kol Nidre*. The prayer begs for release from promises made to God that were not kept during the past year. At the end of Yom Kippur services, atonement for the past year is completed, and a new year begins. A candle burns in the home for the 24 hours of Yom Kippur.

One of the most festive Jewish holidays is *Purim*. It is in celebration of the deed of Esther as told in the Bible. The Book of Esther tells the story of an evil man named Haman who planned to kill all the Jews in Persia. Esther, the queen of Persia, begged the king to help the Jews. He did, and Haman was put to death. In the synagogue on Purim, the Book of Esther is read. Every time the name of Haman is mentioned, the children stamp their feet and shake noisemakers. Gifts are also given on Purim. In the past, children often dressed in costume on this day.

Hanukkah is a festival which lasts for eight days. It is sometimes called the Feast of Lights. It occurs in

December, and is a joyous occasion. Hanukkah celebrates the victory of the Maccabees over the Syrian king Antiochus. According to Jewish history, Antiochus tried to force the Jews into paganism, and to destroy the Jewish people. Led by Judas Maccabeus, the Jews defeated Antiochus. They returned to Jerusalem to rededicate their temple. The Jews found only enough sacred oil to burn for one day. Yet the oil somehow burned for eight days. Hanukkah is celebrated for eight days because of this miracle.

Each night of the eight nights of Hanukkah, a candle is lit, and prayers are said. The eight candles are held in a candelabra called a *menorah*.

Hanukkah is a time for happy celebrations. There are parties. Gifts are given. Special games are played, like the "dreidel" games. The dreidel is a spinning top with four sides. Each side has a letter of the Hebrew alphabet printed on it.

The most famous Jewish holiday is *Passover*. It celebrates the flight of the Jewish people from slavery

as told in the Bible's Book of Exodus. Led by Moses, the Jews came to the Promised Land to begin a new life of freedom.

Passover occurs in March or April each year. It lasts for eight days. Some groups of Jewish people, however, only observe seven days. The eighth day was not added until the Middle Ages.

The most important part of the Passover celebration is *Seder*. It consists of both a religious service and a meal. Special foods and wines are served. During the eight days no leavened bread—which is bread made with yeast — may be eaten. The people eat *matzoh*, an unleavened bread. On the table are symbols of Passover — a roasted lamb bone and a roasted egg.

Prayers are said and the story of Exodus is read. These are contained in a book of worship called the *Haggadah*. As part of the ceremony, the youngest child asks four questions about Passover. The questions are always the same, and the answers are contained in the Haggadah.

Passover is a special holiday for children. They take an active part in the celebrations. And it serves to remind them of the history of their people.

Moslem Holidays

PERHAPS THE LONGEST HOLIDAY in the world is the Moslem feast *Ramadan*, which lasts for a month!

Like Christians and Jews, Moslems all over the world celebrate religious holidays. They are members of the religion called *Islam*, and there are Moslems (or Mohammedans) in Pakistan, Egypt, Iran, and many other parts of Asia and Africa.

For the entire month of Ramadan, Moslems do not eat or drink during the day — but they have a wonderful feast each night. The rules for the holiday are written in the *Koran*, the Moslems' holy book. Following the rules carefully is an important part of being a good Moslem. People spend much time in the *mosque*, praying and reading the *Koran*. The last three days of Ramadan are joyous holidays when people exchange gifts, wear new clothes, and have fairs and family parties.

During the rest of the year, Moslems celebrate holidays that honor many prophets and historical figures that Christians and Jews know from the Bible.

Moslems, in fact, celebrate Adam's Birthday every Friday. They have holidays to honor Moses, Joseph, David, and Abraham, too. They believe that Abraham's second son, Ishmael, was the father of all Arabs, and that his first son, Isaac, was the father of all Jewish people. The day to honor Ishmael and Abraham is called "The Festival." People honor their dead and visit cemeteries, but they also celebrate joyously.

One holiday called *Ashura* celebrates the landing of Noah's ark. They tell the story that Noah's wife was so happy to see land that she made the best and biggest pudding in the world, with dates, raisins, figs, nuts, and currants! On Ashura, Moslem wives try to make a pudding as delicious as the one Noah's wife made.

Ashura is the last and only happy day of the long Moslem New Year, called *Muharram.* In different countries, Moslems celebrate differently—some sadly, some happily. One Moslem New Year belief is that a wonderful lotus tree is at the edge of Paradise. Each leaf bears the name of a person—one leaf for every person in the world. On the first day of the new year, they say, an angel shakes the tree. Some leaves fall. These are the people who will die during the year. So the New Year is a rather sad time. People wear black clothes, go to the mosque, and pray for the dead.

Muharram also observes another sad time—the death, or martyrdom, of Hussein, an early leader of Islam. There are plays showing the battle in which

Hussein died, and people weep and faint with grief. Sometimes they threaten the actor who plays the soldier who killed Hussein.

As Christians celebrate Christmas, the birthday of Christ, Moslems honor the *Birthday of the Prophet*, Mohammed. For nine days there are fairs, feasting, and parades. Stories are told about how the mountains danced when Mohammed was born, and sang, "There is no god but Allah." The trees answered, "And Mohammed is his Prophet." Then 7,000 angels brought a golden vase filled with heavenly dew, and his mother bathed the new baby in it. Many stories like these are told to Arab children on the Prophet's Birthday, the happiest day in the Moslem year.

European Holidays

EUROPE IS A CONTINENT with many countries. They have different languages, histories, and cultures.

Each country has its own heroes and its own special holidays. Certain holidays—Christmas and New Year's Day, for example—are celebrated by all countries in Europe. But there are certain holidays which have special meaning for just one country alone.

In France, the most important holiday of the year is Bastille Day. It is celebrated on July 14th. The Bastille was a large fortress in Paris that was used as a prison during the French Revolution. The French people were fighting for their independence, just as the people in America did during their Revolutionary War. On July 14, 1789, the French people attacked and destroyed the Bastille. Their success led to victory and freedom.

The biggest celebration is in Paris, but Bastille Day is also celebrated throughout the rest of France. Huge parades and fireworks displays are seen everywhere. Carnivals and dances sometimes last through the entire night. In Paris, there is a large torchlight parade on the eve of Bastille Day. The next morning 100 cannons are fired as a salute to the brave men who won freedom for France.

The people of France also celebrate the feast of Joan of Arc. Joan was a young maiden who led the French army against the English at the battle of Orleans in 1429. She saved France from the English. Joan, however, had made many enemies. She was later accused of being a witch, and was burned at the stake in a small

town called Rouen. Today, she is considered a martyr and is honored all over France on her feast day.

Germany is known for its religious celebrations. On almost all of the Christian holidays, the Germans hold fairs, carnivals, dances, and parades.

The most famous festival is held in Munich. It is called the Munich *Oktoberfest.* It is a carnival which lasts for 16 days. Men and women in gay, colorful costumes parade through the fields around Munich. The costumes and dresses represent the clothes worn in Germany throughout history. Horsedrawn wagons carry food and great red casks of beer. There are games, plays, sports, and dances.

Spain is a country where almost everyone is Roman Catholic. Their most important holidays are religious. Holy Week, the week before Easter, is the time of the biggest celebrations. Great parades are held throughout Spain. Mourners in dark hoods march to the pounding of drums. Holy images are carried through the streets, and services are held in the churches.

In the city of Seville, one of the largest and most impressive parades is held. The procession includes groups of carved statues depicting scenes from the life of Christ, carried through the streets on platforms. They are called *pasos*, and some of the statues were carved hundreds of years ago.

Spaniards also celebrate patriotic holidays. A national holiday on April 1st commemorates the end of the Spanish Civil War in 1939. And July 18th celebrates the beginning of that same war of revolution.

One of the most interesting Spanish festivals is the Run of the Bulls at Pamplona. The festival lasts from July 7th to July 14th. Bulls are turned loose in the city and charge through the streets to the Bull Ring. The men of the city run before the bulls, trying des-

perately to avoid the sharp horns of the stampeding bulls. After the bulls are in the ring, the famous Spanish bull fights are held.

Italy is another country where the most important holidays are in honor of religious events. Easter and Holy Week are a time for great processions. And many towns and villages have their own patron saint, whose feast day is a time of great celebration. In the town of Cocullo, a statue of the patron saint, Dominic, is covered with live snakes and carried in a parade.

The feast of Corpus Christi is one of the most important holidays in Italy. It occurs 60 days after Easter. The holiday is marked by beautiful processions. Young girls spread flowers in the path of the Holy Eucharist as it is carried through the streets.

In Scandinavia, people celebrate the end of the long, cold winter with spring and summer holidays. Midsummer's Eve, in June, has been celebrated for thousands of years in Sweden, Norway, Denmark, and Finland. People light huge bonfires. Gay parties go on till morning, for in midsummer, the "midnight sun" shines brightly nearly all night long.

May 1st, or *May Day*, is the traditional day to welcome spring. In Finland, trees are decorated with ribbons and streamers. Students at Uppsala University in Sweden hold a May Day race, celebrating both May Day, the end of school, and an old holiday called Walpurgis Night.

Patriotic holidays, like the birthdays of the kings and queens, are celebrated in Scandinavia. On Norway's Constitution Day, May 17th, schoolchildren march to the royal palace carrying flags. The king and prince greet the crowds of people. And the biggest Fourth of July celebration outside the United States is held in Denmark!

May Day in the Soviet Union honors workers, not springtime. It is International Labor Day, both in Russia and in other Communist nations. Crowds jam Red Square in Moscow to watch huge parades. Russians also hold huge celebrations in October and November to mark the anniversary of their Revolution in 1917.

Holidays in Great Britain

THE BRITISH ISLES include four countries — England, Ireland, Scotland and Wales. Over the years, many people from these countries have immigrated to the United States. They have brought many customs and traditions which are now part of our celebration of holidays. Yet in the British Isles they celebrate many holidays which belong only to them.

In England, the greatest celebration is the coronation of a new king or queen. This holiday may happen only once or twice within an Englishman's lifetime. But when it does occur, it is a great occasion.

The ceremonies are attended by people from all over the world. Other kings and queens, government leaders, and famous people from all walks of life come to London for the coronation. There are balls, parties, and parades. Hundreds of different uniforms are worn. Members of the House of Lords arrive in robes trimmed in ermine. Native costumes are worn by the dignitaries from other countries. And, of course, the British

soldiers and guards wear their brightly colored uniforms. The climax is the crowning of the new king or queen.

The birthday of the king or queen of England is also a holiday. In fact, the birthday of one of England's most famous queens, Victoria, is still celebrated each year. It is May 24th, and is called Empire Day or Commonwealth Day. In the past, an old custom for celebrating this holiday was for the English to dress in the native costume of different English colonies, like India, Australia, Canada, and even Zanzibar.

England also honors an event which never happened. Guy Fawkes Day is a holiday observed throughout England. It celebrates the "not-happening" of the Gunpowder Plot of 1605. Guy Fawkes, a treacherous villain, and his followers planned to blow up the king and Parliament. Fawkes was caught just as he was about to light the fuse on several crates of gunpowder, which were placed under the House of Lords. The plot failed and Guy Fawkes was executed the next year. On November 5th each year, the English celebrate this event which fortunately did not happen. Bonfires are set ablaze, and in many places "effigies" of Guy Fawkes are burned.

The Irish have a very special day, March 17th—
St. Patrick's Day. St. Patrick is the patron saint of Ireland,
even though he was not born there. St. Patrick came to
Ireland in the fifth century. He brought religion to the
island, and is said to have worked many miracles. The
most famous story of St. Patrick is that he drove all the
snakes out of Ireland. It is said that St. Patrick held up a
shamrock and all the snakes fled for their lives.

St. Patrick's Day is celebrated with parades and
parties. The biggest parade is held in Dublin, but
parties are held everywhere.

Scotland also honors its patron saint—St. Andrew.
On November 30th, his birthday is celebrated. It is
a day for feasting. The traditional dish is *haggis*, which
is like pudding and is cooked, of all places, in the belly
of a sheep.

Young men and young women trade vows of love
on the eve of St. Andrew's Day. And today, many a
Scotsman celebrates this holiday with a game of golf.

But there is no disrespect for St. Andrew, because he is said to have invented the game.

The country of Wales celebrates many unusual festivals. The *Eisteddfod* is a music festival held each August. It is a very important gathering for the music-loving Welsh.

The first Eisteddfod was held in the 6th century. Mostly *bards* (poets) and minstrels, who roamed about the country in those days, attended the festival. Contests in poetry, music, and folk songs were held. Today, singers, poets, dancers and musicians from all over the country arrive. The festival formally begins with the blowing of trumpets. The music, singing, and contests begin. There is beautiful music everywhere.

Holidays in Canada

CANADA, OUR NORTHERN neighbor, has close ties with Great Britain. *Dominion Day*, July 1st, honors the day in 1867 when Canada became a nation and a member of the British Commonwealth. It is the celebration of their independence, and the festivities are much like ours of July 4th. When the weather is warm, picnics and outings are common. In the capital of Canada, Ottawa, and in the capitals of all the provinces, July 1st is a day for speeches and colorful parades.

The English who settled in Canada brought with them the celebration of *Boxing Day* on December 26th. Despite its name, the day does not honor the sport made famous by Jack Dempsey, Joe Louis, and Rocky Marciano. Instead, it is a day for giving gifts to others

who perform services during the year. To most Canadians today, Boxing Day provides a welcome rest from the excitement of Christmas Day. Originally, it was a day for the wealthy people of England to prepare "boxes" of gifts for their servants and other poor people. For people receiving "boxes," Boxing Day is Christmas, one day late!

The American holiday of Thanksgiving has traveled across the border to Canada. Each year, an official government proclamation declares a day in October which is to be set aside to give thanks for all the blessings received during the year. On the Canadian Thanksgiving, church services and a splendid turkey dinner with all the trimmings are traditional.

Latin American Holidays

FIESTA TIME! Nearly every day of the year is a holiday for some of our neighbors in Mexico and Latin America. In villages and small towns in every country, processions and parades are held to celebrate special occasions. There are religious festivals to honor many of the saints, because nearly all the people of Latin America belong to the Roman Catholic Church.

Some of these holidays are celebrated in only a few towns. Others are special occasions for people in all the many countries in South America, Central America, Mexico, and some islands in the Caribbean.

Corpus Christi Day in June is one of the most important and popular religious holidays. There are many solemn and religious parts to the celebration, and many that are not solemn or religious. "Devil dancers" roam the streets in Venezuela and Panama, shaking rattles and wearing frightening masks with horns. The idea of having parades of giants, dragons, and little devils was brought from Spain by the early settlers.

In Peru, the Corpus Christi holiday goes on for several weeks. Images or statues of favorite saints are carried into the city and are left overnight in the cathedral. The story is that once the people have left, the statues have their own festival, dancing and having fun just as ordinary people do.

Mexican children love Corpus Christi Day because they can wear special costumes. In Mexico, this holiday has become a special occasion for different kinds of workers—house builders, weavers, pottery

makers. There are miniature markets where tiny houses and tiny loaves of bread are sold, and restaurants serving tiny bites of food in what look like doll dishes. Everything is paid for with play money or pieces of candy. In other towns, though, there are parades in which everything is very big. Bakers carry huge bread loaves, and guitar makers carry guitars six feet long!

Midsummer Eve, in the middle of June, was one of the most important ancient European holidays. The Spanish and Portuguese brought this important

146

festival with them, and it was changed and mixed with the customs of the ancient Indians of South America. In Latin America, this holiday is called *St. John's Day*, but many customs are older than Christianity.

In many countries, people build huge bonfires to honor the sun's fire on St. John's Day. Couples dance around the bonfires. In parts of Paraguay, people walk through the live coals barefoot! In Mexico, paraders wear the feathered costumes that the Aztecs wore before the Spaniards came. They beat a huge drum and play old flutes and rattles. In other parts of Mexico, the holiday is a religious festival of John the Baptist.

Throughout all of Latin America, May 3rd is *Dia de la Cruz*, or the Day of the Holy Cross. Roadside crosses and shrines are decorated with flowers. People build special altars and crosses in their homes or gardens, and decorate them with flowers, paper decorations, statues, and ribbons.

For Mexican workmen and builders, the Day of the Holy Cross is a very special day. On the highest peak of any building being built, they erect a cross decorated with colored streamers, flags, and flowers. Firecrackers

and rockets explode all day, and sometimes small groups of musicians serenade the workers!

February 2nd, which most Americans know as Groundhog Day, is a religious holiday in many countries. It is called Candlemas or, in Spanish-speaking countries, *Candelaría*. The South American countries in the Andes Mountains, where there are many Indians, celebrate this holiday with fiestas that last for a week or more.

In the churches, candles for the coming year are blessed. Outside, in the streets and the markets, hundreds of people dance to the beat of drums. The Indian women wear many layers of bright-colored full skirts, dark shawls, and derby hats! Other dancers wear costumes—bullfighters' suits, animal skins, and costumes like the Spanish conquerors wore.

The day that we celebrate as Halloween is the beginning of a two-day religious holiday in most of Latin America. All Saints Day and All Souls Day, which come on November 1st and 2nd, honor those who have died. All Souls Day is also called "Day of the Dead," and Latin Americans make trips to cemeteries with flowers, candles, and even food. But when the solemnity is over, the Day of the Dead becomes very lively indeed, and there is dancing and a fiesta. In Mexico, it is believed that the dead need a vacation, and return to earth to take part in the celebration. So altars are built, and food is spread for these visiting "souls." Bakeries sell small sugar candies shaped like skulls, and many other toys that look like coffins or skeletons.

A special patron saint for Mexican children is San Antonio Abad. On his feast day, every child dresses up his favorite pet to be blessed by the priest in church. You might meet a cow painted with red and white stripes, a puppy wearing velvet pants and a hat, or a burro wearing a big bow tie—for pets must look their best on this special day.

Most of the Latin American countries have an "independence day" like our Fourth of July. They celebrate the birthdays of heroes like Bolivar and Juarez, as we celebrate American heroes' birthdays.

On the night of September 15th, 1821, Father Miguel Hidalgo stood on a balcony in a small Mexican town and called upon the people to rise in a revolution against the Spanish government. Independence came a year later. Now every year, his speech, called the *grito*, is repeated on that night in every city and town. In Mexico City, the President himself speaks from the National Palace. At midnight, all the bells in the cathedrals, along with factory whistles and automobile horns, welcome Independence Day, September 16th. There are parades and fireworks.

Mexicans also celebrate *Cinco de Mayo*, the Fifth of May, which is the day of a famous and important battle against the French in 1892. They stage a mock battle, with half the players dressed as famous Mexican generals and soldiers, and the others as French and Indian soldiers.

Independence Day in Peru comes on July 28th, when there are special bullfights and games. A week later, Bolivians celebrate their *Independencia* with masquerades, Indian dances, and carnivals. Rodeos are popular during Chile's independence day, September 18th. The *huaso*, Chile's cowboy, wears a broad-brimmed hat, fringed black leather leggings, and a wildly striped short cape.

Chinese Holidays

EVERY CHINESE BOY AND GIRL celebrates a birthday on the very same day of the year—the Chinese New Year. Traditionally, it is the merriest and most important holiday of the whole year. All Chinese children have other birthdays, too, of course—but part of the New Year's festival is a big birthday party.

Chinese New Year comes at the beginning of the *lunar* year (a different way of figuring time), which is usually early in February in our calendar. In the United States, many people whose families are Chinese still celebrate this holiday and January 1st too.

Chinese New Year is a 15-day holiday. People clean and paint their houses—and buy new clothes if they can.

On New Year's Day it is bad luck to step on the ground wearing old shoes!

Even before the New Year begins, Chinese families get their houses ready. The old paper image of the "Kitchen God" is given a goodbye dinner of sweet foods so he will say only sweet things about the family. Then the paper image is burned, along with bright-colored paper chariots the children have made. The "Kitchen God" travels off to heaven in a cloud of fire, and popping fireworks wish him a happy trip.

A new "Kitchen God" arrives with the New Year, and the master of the house sets up a new image, made of bright red, green, and yellow paper.

Before the New Year starts, everyone pays every penny they owe to anybody. On New Year's Eve, families seal their doors with good-luck charms and have a solemn meal to say good-bye to the old year. Children bow to their parents and wish them "Happy New Year."

The New Year ends with the Feast of Lanterns, when a huge paper dragon leads a joyful parade through the streets. As many as 100 men and boys carry the dragon—and a Chinese boy knows he is grown up when he is big enough to help carry the dragon.

Like nearly all people everywhere, the Chinese have always celebrated the arrival of spring. There are

many different spring holidays. *Li Chum*, the happiest
holiday, comes at the beginning of the spring planting
season. All the country people celebrate and pray
for good rice crops and rich harvests. In parades,
everybody carries flowers. And they honor the water
buffalo. This animal plays such a big part in farming
that he is the symbol of spring. When the people come
home from the fields, they go to traditional plays or
"plum-blossom" parties. Many go to weddings, because
Li Chum is supposed to be a lucky day to get married.

Other spring holidays also involve the growing
crops. *Yu Shui*, in late February, celebrates "spring

showers." *Ching Chi,* in March, means "The insects are stirring." Farmers run to the fields and destroy the insects who might ruin the new crops.

The Chinese have always honored their families and ancestors highly. Their "Memorial Day" is called *Ching Ming*—or the Pure and Bright Festival. They decorate cemeteries with willow twigs, and put offerings of food on their family graves. Then the living family has a picnic. Because Ching Ming is also the first real day of spring, people often plant trees on this day, too. It is a respectful holiday, but full of joy.

Japanese Holidays

JAPANESE BOYS AND GIRLS have two holidays that are especially for children.

Hina Matsuri, March 3rd, is a doll festival for girls. The family's doll collection, sometimes very old and always very beautiful, is displayed on special shelves. The emperor and empress dolls, of course, have the top shelf. Dolls dressed like court gentlemen, ladies-in-waiting, pages, and musicians sit on the lower shelves. The dolls are the hosts and hostesses for friends who visit the girls in each family. A tiny tea table is set out in front of each doll's shelf.

Doll's Day is also the Peach Blossom Festival. These flowers mean beauty and gentleness, and a branch is usually put on the shelf with the dolls.

On Boy's Day, May 5th, families who have sons fly huge paper fish on a tall pole in the garden—one for

each boy. The boys are told about the bravery and courage of their families. They are given swords or suits of armor or banners with family mottoes on them.

There are kite-flying contests and kite "battles" all during the spring and summer in Japan. One of the biggest of these kite battles is held on Boy's Day. The story of the kite-flying contests is that, hundreds of years ago, the feudal lord of Hamamatsu was so happy at the birth of his baby son that he wrote the baby's name on a huge kite so that everyone would know about it. In a five-day festival, boys of Hamamatsu battle with kites in the air. Sharp bits of glass glued to each kite string make the battle very exciting.

May 5th is also a national holiday called "Children's Day," and all Japanese children are wished happiness and prosperity.

Many Japanese holidays are religious. Since many Japanese are Buddhists, there are beautiful festivals and dances at Buddhist temples. Many other Japanese belong to the religion called *Shinto*, and have their own festivals and holidays. Still others are Christians, who observe Christmas and other Christian holidays.

Some very old holidays are nature holidays. They are held at the beginning of the rice-growing and fishing seasons and at harvest time. In one town, young girls in beautiful, old-fashioned kimonos plant the first rice seedlings, while other people chant and sing. In another town, the women rule the first days of the rice-planting. They take wooden buckets, fill them with mud from the rice paddies, and throw mud at every man they meet.

The Festival of Lanterns, or *Bon Matsuri,* is one of the biggest holidays of the year. Buddhists in Japan have celebrated it for about 1500 years.

During the Feast of Lanterns, which occurs in the middle of July, Buddhists honor members of the family who have died, including all their ancestors for thousands of years. On the first day, families take lanterns to the cemeteries to guide the spirits back to earth for the festival. Food is put on altars in the houses. On the third day, families say farewell to the spirits who have visited them. Thousands of tiny lantern-boats are set afloat on the lakes and on the ocean. Each one has a Japanese letter written on its sail.

Though Bon Matsuri honors the dead, it is not a sad time. There is dancing and singing, especially in the villages.

Japan became a democracy after World War II, and added a new holiday to its calendar—Constitution Day, May 3rd. The emperor and empress and important public officials meet in a ceremony at the entrance to the Imperial Palace in Tokyo.

Another new national holiday falls on November 23rd—it is called Labor-Thanksgiving Day. Japan has borrowed from the United States the ideas of Labor Day, when workers are honored, and Thanksgiving, when people are thankful for what they have. The Japanese have combined them into this one new holiday.

A new and solemn Japanese holiday is the *Peace Festival* held each year in Hiroshima, where the first atomic bomb was dropped in 1945. The ceremony honors those killed, and prayers are said for peace in the world. People sing songs of peace and send small lantern-boats down the river.

Holidays in India

THOUGH INDIA IS VERY OLD, it has been an independent nation for just a little over 20 years. In 1947, after being a British colony for many years, the huge country gained the right to rule itself. Today Indians celebrate Independence Day, August 15th, with pageants and parades. Republic Day, January 26th, is another patriotic holiday, marking the day India joined the British Commonwealth.

India also has many religious holidays. Its 300 million Hindus have so many festivals that two or three sometimes fall on the same day. Indian Christians, Jains, Sikhs, Moslems, and other religious groups observe their own holidays.

The Hindu festival *Divali*, "the garland of lights," is a five-in-one holiday. Five separate festivals come in a row. To get ready, Indians scrub and paint their houses and hang garlands of flowers in the doorways.

On the first night, hundreds of little oil lamps are lighted. They are hung on the walls and parapets of every house, where they will burn throughout Divali. They will light the way for Lakshmi, goddess of wealth, to visit every home. When the lamps are lit, every building is outlined with little flickering lights.

Each day of Divali honors a different Hindu god. People tell old stories about these gods and heroes. Everyone tries to have new clothes and to bathe in a flowing river, which Hindus consider holy.

The gayest and wildest of Hindu holidays is the spring festival called *Holi*. Indian boys collect all the fuel they can for the huge Holi bonfire. When the moon rises, the fires are lit. Drums boom and horns blow. Soon people are dancing around the fire singing folk songs. Crowds chase each other through the streets, throwing colored paint and yelling. At sunrise the fire is put out, and everyone marks his forehead with the ashes. Sometimes Holi goes on for more than a week, as people celebrate the coming of spring.

There are thousands of other Hindu festivals. Many honor old beliefs in the gods of the sun, moon, stars, and the spirits in plants and animals. All living things, in fact, are sacred to Hindus. Very holy men eat no meat at all, and no Hindu would kill a sacred cow. There are also millions of Hindu gods—but Hindus believe these are all different forms of one

"trinity." The gods in the trinity are *Brahma* the Creator, *Vishnu* the Preserver, and *Siva* the Destroyer.

One important holiday is the *Durga Puja,* in the autumn, which honors Siva's wife. All the houses, even very poor ones, have a statue of Durga. She is very tall, with ten arms, and rides a sacred lion. Since Durga is a mother-goddess, her holiday is also a festival for mothers. Pageants, plays, and celebrations are held the entire time, ending with a display of fireworks.

Can you imagine a day on which you honored your schoolbooks, your mother her broom, and your father his pencil or typewriter or hammer? Hindus have a Festival of Tools, to honor the god Visvakarma. Everyone puts an important tool before a pitcher that represents the god. Gardeners bring rakes. Artists bring brushes. Housewives bring brooms.

Then each person lights a candle. They give thanks for the help the tools have given them, and ask them to do good work in the coming year. Sometimes they add flowers or incense to the altar. After that, the day is a happy holiday for workers.

159

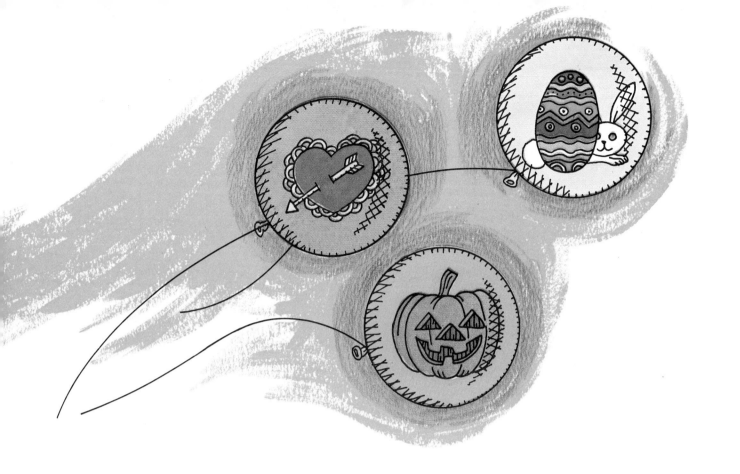

Parties and Entertaining

Time for a Party

PARTIES ARE A LOT OF FUN—both to give and to go to. But parties are the most fun when they are planned right. Maybe you would like to give a party for a very special occasion, but are not quite sure how. Or maybe you would just like to give a party—and need a good idea.

Many parties are for special occasions. They may be for a *birthday* or a *graduation*, for someone who is moving away, or for someone new in your school or your neighborhood. There are lots of holidays all through the year that are also good reasons to give a party. Here is a calendar for party-giving, which you can use for your own parties, for class parties at school, or for parties that your scout troop or cub den or any other group wants to give.

Spring Parties
St. Patrick's Day (March 17)   May Day (May 1)
Easter   End of School Parties
April Fool's Day (April 1)

Summer Parties
Memorial Day (May 30)   Picnics
Flag Day (June 14)   Barbecues
Independence Day (July 4)   Outdoor Parties
Labor Day (September)

Autumn Parties
Columbus Day (Oct. 12)   Hay Rides
Halloween (Oct. 31)   Hikes
Thanksgiving (November)   Square Dances

Winter Parties
Christmas (Dec. 25)   Lincoln's Birthday (Feb. 12)
New Year's (Dec. 31-Jan. 1)   Valentine's Day (Feb. 14)
Martin Luther King Day   Washington's Birthday (Feb. 22)
  (January)   Ice-skating or sledding
Groundhog Day (Feb. 2)   Caroling

How To Be a Host or Hostess

WHEN YOU DECIDE TO GIVE a party, you become someone special. You are no longer just Jack or Jane or Susan or Kevin—you are a *host* or a *hostess*.

There are certain things that you, as the host or hostess, should do.

Planning the party. Find out from your mother how many guests you may invite. Then decide which friends to ask, what time the party will be, and what kind of food to serve. Then decide if you want to have special favors or decorations. You may buy them or make them. (Pages 178-185 give you some ideas.)

Sending out invitations. Pages 166-167 show some invitations you can make yourself. If the party is to be a small one for close friends, you can telephone the invitations. Always tell *what day, what time, where,* and any special reason for the party. The guests will

want to know what kind of clothes to wear—dress-up, school clothes, play clothes, or costumes.

Greeting guests. Answer the door when guests begin to arrive, and say hello to each guest. If the guests' mothers or fathers bring them to the party, the host and hostess say hello to them, too, and ask them to come in. In cold weather, the host or hostess takes people's coats and boots and scarves and puts them away.

Introducing people. Sometimes you may invite friends from school that your mother does not know. When they arrive, you say something like, "Mother, I'd like you to meet Jane, who is in my geography class." Perhaps your friend's mother or father is at the door, too. Your friend should introduce you, just the way you would introduce your mother. But if your friend does not do this, then you introduce yourself, something like this: "I'm Sue, Mrs. Whitman. And this is my mother, Mrs. Anderson. Would you like to come in for a minute?"

Finding something for everyone to do. As the host or hostess, you start games that other people can join as they arrive. If you are very busy, you can ask a good friend to answer the door as other guests come in.

164

At parties for young children (preschoolers), "games" will usually be familiar songs and playing with toys. Mother, of course, will be this party's hostess. She makes certain that no one is left out of the games, and helps shy children join the fun.

But if you are older, you should be your own host or hostess as much as you can. It's *your* party and *your* friends, not your mother's!

Pages 171-177 give you some ideas for games. Probably you know many more. Maybe you and your friends enjoy other things, too, like singing songs you all know. Plan your games ahead of time, though, so that you don't have a roomful of people just sitting—or, worse yet, a roomful of boys or girls who have started to fight or yell because they don't have anything else to do.

Helping your mother at the party. You should plan with your mother what time the food will be served. When it is time, you should help her bring the food in. Make sure all the guests have been served before filling up your own plate and cup.

Saying good-bye to every guest. If mothers or fathers are calling for guests, you say hello at the door just as you did at the beginning of the party.

The host or hostess never sits and plays when guests are going home. If it is your birthday party, you should be sure to say "thank you" for your presents.

Helping to clean up. When you are the host or hostess it is your job to clear plates and cups from the table. You put away decorations, and any toys or games or records that are left out. You also pick up anything spilled on the floor—and you offer to wash the dishes.

Party Invitations

THE GUESTS WHO ARE COMING to your party need to know three important things—where it is, what time it is, and what kind of party it is.

If it is just a small party for friends you know very well, you can call them on the telephone to invite them. If it is a special party or if you are asking many guests, invitations should be sent.

You can buy invitations that have spaces for you (or your mother) to write in what your guests need to know—the time, the day, the place.

Invitations you make yourself are fun, too. You can use small cards or construction paper. For a Valentine's Day party, for instance, you could use red hearts cut out of red construction paper. For Christmas you could make snowmen, or bells, or green trees. A big orange pumpkin or black witch hat would be a good Halloween party invitation.

On written invitations, be sure to say if the guests should wear costumes or certain kinds of clothes (for a picnic or a skating party, for instance).

Sometimes you get invitations that have the letters "RSVP" or the words "Please reply" written in one corner. This means that you should call or write the person who sent the invitation and tell them whether you can go to their party. Even if these words are not on the invitation, it is much more polite to tell your host or hostess if you can come. But if the words are there, *be sure* to answer the invitation.

167

Party Food

HALF THE FUN OF A PARTY is eating special treats—cake and ice cream, or hot dogs and hamburgers, or whatever you like best!

Party treats are half the fun for your guests, too, so think carefully when you are planning the food and refreshments for your party. Talk over the *menu*—the food you will serve—with your mother. If you are used to helping in the kitchen, be sure to do all you can to help get the party food ready.

At many parties, especially birthdays, you may not serve a real meal. Instead, there will probably be a birthday cake with candles, and ice cream. Small, decorated paper cups with nuts or candies are nice to put at each person's plate.

If you want to have more than that, try to think of things that are both easy to make and good to eat. You can make *sandwiches* before the party starts, choosing things that both you and your friends like to eat. Peanut butter and jelly, cheese, chicken salad, and tuna salad are all good sandwiches. Nearly everyone likes hot dogs and hamburgers, but if you are having many people, be sure to ask your mother if she is willing to do all that cooking!

You and your friends probably like cakes, cookies, and ice cream. Cake and cookies are really very easy to make. For a party at Christmas time, you can make gingerbread men or cut-out cookies in the shapes of bells, trees, or a Santa Claus. For Lincoln's or Washington's birthday, you can make a "Lincoln log" or a

"cherry tree branch" from a chocolate cookie roll, made with cookie crumbs and whipped cream or ice cream.

A big, beautiful birthday cake with candles on it is one of the most exciting parts of a birthday party. But small cupcakes are fun, too, and you can decorate them for special kinds of parties. Use colored coconut and little candy eggs to make a "nest" for an Easter party. Or use pink icing and little candy hearts for a Valentine party. For Halloween, you could use orange icing and devil's food cupcakes.

Milk or soft drinks go well with cake or cookies. (Remember to have plenty in your refrigerator.) But maybe you would like something different. For summer parties, you could serve lemonade, pink lemonade, or even a tasty pink fruit punch made with pink fruit juice, lemonade, and ginger ale. For fall and winter, bright red cranberry juice, golden apple juice, or sweet cider are good. Best of all, don't forget that after a skating party or caroling there is nothing finer than hot cocoa with marshmallows floating on top!

Party Games

CHOOSING THE RIGHT KIND of party games is a very important part of making sure that everyone at a party has fun. Here are some things to think about in choosing games to play at your party.

How old are the boys and girls who will be there? This may be the most important question. For very young children, and for most preschoolers, organized games are not always possible. Perhaps the whole group will be able to play some singing games like "London Bridge" or "Farmer in the Dell," but most games should be saved for older children.

Also, some games that delight 6- and 7-year-olds may bore their 9- or 10-year-old brothers and sisters. Probably you know best what you and your friends like to do—so choose your games carefully.

Is the party to be held indoors or outdoors? In a house or an apartment? Where your party will be decides how lively and noisy the games can be. In the summer, a back yard or patio is the ideal place for all parties. If your house has a game room or family room, you have a good place for winter parties, too. But if you do not have much space—an apartment or a small house—you should plan to keep the number of guests fairly small and organize the whole party very carefully.

Check with your mother to see where you can have the party—and where the guests should not go.

Does your party have a theme—birthday, patriotic, seasonal? Many traditional and popular party games can be changed to fit the special theme of your party.

PIN THE TAIL

The oldest version of this game is "Pin the Tail on the Donkey," but the possibilities for variations are almost endless. Some are:

      Pin the Hat (or Smile) on the Clown
      Pin the Beard on Santa Claus
      Pin the Broom on the Witch

BALLOON GAMES

Balloon Hockey: Players use brooms to sweep balloons across the other team's "goal line."

Balloon Tennis: Players keep balloons in the air using their hands. Each team uses a different color balloon, and the team that keeps its balloon up longest is the winner.

Balloon Relay: In "relay" games, the team members play one at a time. In this game, one member of each team runs up to a chair, blows up a balloon, and then breaks it by sitting on it! The team that breaks all its balloons first is the winner.

GOSSIP (TELEPHONE)

This is usually a game for girls, and can be played while guests are sitting around a table. The girl at the head of the table whispers a "message" just once to the girl next to her. That girl passes it on to her neighbor, and so on around the entire group. The one at the end repeats the message as she heard it—which is usually not at all like the first message.

TREASURE HUNT

Several peanuts, buttons, or Easter eggs (or any other small objects) are hidden around the room or the house before the party begins. Whoever finds the most during the party is the winner.

ANIMAL CHARADES

One player, or one team, chooses an animal to act out. The others must guess what he is supposed to be.

SIMON SAYS

All players sit in front of the leader, who calls out instructions: "Stand up." "Simon says sit down." "Wave your hand." "Simon says whistle."

The trick, of course, is that only when "Simon says" an order should it be followed. Players who follow an order without "Simon says" are out of the game. The player who remains in the game longest is the winner.

MUSICAL CHAIRS

You need a phonograph or piano for this game. There should be one less chair than there are players. Everyone marches or skips around the chairs while the music is playing. When it stops, everyone rushes to get a chair. The person without a chair is "out." The next time the music starts, one more chair is taken away. The game goes on until there are only two players—and just one chair. The one who gets the final chair is the winner.

HOT AND COLD

While one person is out of the room, the others choose an object—a chair, someone's shoe, or anything easily seen. The person who is "It" comes back and tries to find the object. He is given clues of "You're getting warmer (or colder)" as he gets nearer to or farther away from it.

BUTTON, BUTTON

One person is "It," and stands in the center of the circle of players. All players move their hands behind their backs as if they were passing something to their neighbors, and "It" tries to guess who really has the button. He taps that person's shoulder, and if that player really has the button, he becomes "It."

CAPTAIN, MAY I

This game should be played outdoors or in a fairly large room. Players line up at a distance away from the "captain." He then gives orders to take certain steps. Any player who fails to ask "Captain, may I?" before moving must take penalty steps backwards, as the captain orders. Traditional steps include:

Giant steps—full stride.

Baby steps—one foot directly in front of the other, heel to toe.

Scissors steps—Jump with feet apart, then together.

When the "captain" is not looking, players can "steal" moves forward, but if he catches them they must go back to the starting line. The player who reaches the captain first is the winner.

I'M TAKING A TRIP

The first player starts off the game by saying, "I'm taking a trip to Grandmother's (or anywhere he chooses), and in my suitcase I will pack an *apple*." The second player says the whole thing again, but adds an item starting with "B": "I'm taking a trip to Grandmother's, and I will pack an *apple* and a *bicycle*." The third player adds an item beginning with "C," "I will pack an *apple*, a *bicycle*, and a *cup*." The game goes on until the alphabet is finished, or until all players give up trying to remember the list!

PENCIL AND PAPER GAMES

Word Treasure Hunts: Players are given a certain word to write at the top of their paper, and must see how many other words they can make from its letters in the time limit. Words can be appropriate to the party theme: BIRTHDAY, CHRISTMAS, REINDEER, JACK O'LANTERN, CHERRY TREE, etc.

Changing Words: By changing just one letter at a time, players try to change one short word into another word with a different meaning. "Change FLAG to a word that means a round red vegetable!"

FLAG   FLAT   FEAT   BEAT   BEET

Decorations and Costumes

TO MAKE ANY PARTY look and feel more "partyish," you can buy or make bright-colored decorations. Although many stores sell decorations, it is often more fun to make your own.

The decorations for holiday parties usually follow certain traditional ideas. Parties that are not for any special holiday can be planned around a *theme* or idea. Parties with themes are especially good for group parties—your school class or scout troop, for instance. *Costumes* can make a theme party even more fun.

Use your imagination to think up new party themes. Here are four ideas you can use—Wild West, Astronaut, Zoo or Circus, and Storybook.

Most boys and girls like to dress up as cowboys and Indians. A *Wild West* party lets everyone wear a cowboy suit or an Indian costume. Perhaps you can borrow some lipstick from your mother to draw "war paint" on your face. It is easy to make an Indian headband from paper, with a tall feather stuck in it. Wear moccasins on your feet and borrow several strings of beads from your mother or sister.

For decorations, you can try to make the room look like a corral or an Indian camp. You can roll large sheets of brown paper into a tall cone and paint it to look like a tepee.

Small round ice cream cartons can be painted to look like an Indian drum, or *tomtom*. If you make enough, you can use them as favors on the table. Make a small tepee from a paper cone for the middle of the table.

When you play games at your Wild West party, all the guests in Indian costumes can be one "team" and the "cowboys" can be the other team.

If you would rather be more modern, you can have an *Astronaut* theme for your party. For costumes, you can try to copy the suits you have seen real astronauts wearing. Or maybe you would rather invent your own space suit—one you may someday wear while exploring the planet Mars or the moon.

For table decorations, make a rocket from the cardboard tube from a roll of paper towels. (Ask your mother to save these in her kitchen.) Make a pointed nose-cone to attach to the rocket, paint it silver-gray, and stand it up in the center of the table. Cover the table with dark blue paper sprinkled with cut-out stars.

Everyone loves a *Zoo* or *Circus* party. For the Zoo party, you can dress like your favorite animals. Begin your costume with leotards or tights and a matching shirt of the right color: yellow-brown for the lion or tiger, brown for the monkey, green for the parrot, and so on. Then use paper or cloth to add a tail or ears or wings or whatever you need. You can even cut a mask out of cardboard and paint an animal face.

For a Circus party, you can use animal costumes, and add the clown, the acrobats, and the animal tamer. A pair of pajamas a few sizes too big for you is a good beginning for a clown costume. Add a ruffle around the neck, big shoes, and clown make-up on your face. Acrobats can wear tights and a shirt with spangles added. Girls can wear a bathing suit or ballet costume.

Perhaps you have a clown doll or some stuffed animals that you can use to decorate the table at a Circus or Zoo party. Long strips of red and white crepe paper can make a circus "tent" from the ceiling of the room. For favors, use animal crackers. Tie bunches of balloons to the back of each person's chair.

A *Storybook* party takes a little more work making costumes. Each guest can come as a favorite character from a story, fairy tale, or nursery rhyme. The storybook characters who arrive at this party may be just about anyone—Tom Sawyer, the Cat in the Hat, Alice in Wonderland, Old Mother Hubbard, or Pooh.

To decorate the table, you can choose almost any storybook idea, too. If you can find an old overshoe or workshoe, you can make an "Old Woman in the Shoe" centerpiece. Put as many small dolls as you can into the shoe. Or you can use stuffed dolls that look like Pooh, Piglet, the Peanuts characters, or any other storybook person.

Patriotic holidays—Washington's and Lincoln's Birthdays, Memorial Day, Independence Day call for red, white, and blue, the colors of the flag. Wide crepe paper strips can be used to make bunting around the room and a striped cloth for the table. Cardboard "firecrackers" filled with candy or popcorn make good favors and table decorations. A tiny American flag stuck in a marshmallow can sit at each person's place at the table.

Remember, though, never to drape real American flags or use them carelessly.

The log cabin theme is a good idea for *Lincoln's Birthday,* along with the red, white, and blue flag decorations, because this great president came from a family of poor pioneers.

For *Washington's Birthday,* you can use some of the stories about the first president. The "cherry tree" story is just a story, but your decorations can be small paper hatchets and little bunches of candy cherries.

Halloween parties are usually decorated in orange and black. Witches, black cats, and pumpkins are the favorite decorations. A jack-o-lantern with a big grin can be placed in the middle of the table. Since Halloween is a spooky time, you might want to keep the room dark and mysterious. Hang some of the decorations from the ceiling.

The ideas for costumes for *theme* parties can be used for Halloween costumes, too.

Christmas parties, or any other winter parties, can have snowman decorations. Use marshmallows stuck together with toothpicks to make a big snowman for the table. The table cloth can be red, white, or green crepe paper.

Christmas tree branches and holly are the other traditional Christmas decorations. Put together Christmas tree ornaments and tree branches to make small decorations for other parts of the room. You can make small green trees by cutting tree shapes from green construction paper or rolling the paper into a cone. Use crayons to decorate the trees, and make one for each guest, putting each person's name on his own tree.

For *Valentine's Day*, use red hearts cut from construction paper at each person's place. If you have a big "mailbox" for Valentines, decorate it with white paper, red hearts, and paper lace doilies.

For *Easter* parties, color Easter eggs for each person. Paint or draw their names on each egg. Use pretty colors—green, yellow, violet—to make a crepe paper table cloth. A big Easter basket filled with colored eggs and chocolate eggs is a good centerpiece. If you have a stuffed animal that looks like a rabbit, use it in the center of the table, holding candy eggs in its paws. Put green paper "straw" around it for a nest.

How To Be a Guest

DO YOU HAVE TO DO ANYTHING special when you are a guest? Don't you just go to a party and have a good time? Of course, you have a good time, but you also remember to behave so that other people at the party have a good time, too. "Party manners" do not mean that you have to sit in a corner and not do anything at all. But they do mean that you *think* about what you are doing before you do it.

Chances are that at home you are not supposed to jump on the furniture or chase your brother down the hall or scream at the top of your voice. Even if you are having a wonderful time at someone else's house, don't forget that it is someone's home, too.

When you get to a party, remember to say hello to your friend's mother or to the scout leader or to any other adult who is helping out. Remember to tell them "thank you" and "good-bye" when you leave, too. If you have never met them before, and your friends are busy somewhere else, then introduce yourself.

If you know their name, just say "Mrs. Adams, I am Joey Saunders, Bill's friend." If you don't know who they are, just tell them your own name. They will tell you their name and probably say "I'm Lucy's mother" or "I'm Tom's scoutmaster." Boys and men usually shake hands when they meet. Girls and women sometimes do.

When you are at a party, remember that you are not in charge of it. The boy or girl who is giving it is the one who decides when you will play games and when

you will eat. And they suggest the things to do. (When you give your own party, you can decide these things.)

If someone asks "What would you like to do?" you can suggest your favorite games. But if everyone else wants to play a game that you don't particularly like, be a good sport about it. Probably you *will* like the next game, so don't sulk or refuse to play. That just spoils other people's fun — and it is not one of the ways to be a good guest!

Another rule about being a good guest is "Don't be first or last." When food is served, don't rush into the dining room as if you are afraid someone will eat everything before you get there. On the other hand, don't just sit and wait to be called two or three times. If you have to leave a party early, do it quietly, not upsetting everyone else. But if the party is supposed to end at a certain time, plan to leave then.

If you have to leave a party early, tell your friend's mother: "I'm sorry but I have to leave early because my mother is picking me up at 3:00," or "I have to leave for my piano lesson," or whatever your reason is.

Did you ever hear grown-ups talk about someone "wearing out their welcome?" That is a good way to describe what happens when the last guest at a party waits and waits and doesn't get ready to go home. The people who were very glad to see you earlier now are "worn out." Maybe it is suppertime, or maybe they have other things to do. In any case, when the party is over, it is time for you to go home!

If for some reason, no one will be home at your house until later, have your mother explain this before the party. Then your host or hostess and their parents will be expecting you to stay a little later.

Sometimes you will be invited to spend the night or a weekend or an even longer time at the house of a friend or a relative. Stre-e-etch your regular party manners to cover the entire time you are a guest in someone else's house. Always check with your parents before saying yes to these invitations, so that they will know your plans and can talk them over with the other grown-ups.

When you have stayed at someone's house, it is nicest to write them a "thank-you" note, as well as saying "thank you" when you leave.

Being a good guest is not really hard at all. And the important thing to remember is that with just a little effort you can be the good guest who always gets invited to other parties. Bad guests often are not asked to come again—and so they miss many good parties!

Saying Thank You

BEFORE YOU LEAVE A PARTY, be sure to look for your friend's mother or any other adult who is in charge. Tell her "thank you" and "I had a very good time." If the party is for your friend's birthday, say "Happy Birthday" again before you leave.

Always write notes to your aunts, grandparents, and other people who send you *presents* for your birthday, Christmas, Hanukkah, or any other time. Unless you have a chance to thank them in person, you (not your mother) should write a thank-you letter. It can be very short, if you like. When writing to a friend or relative far away, it will be even nicer to say something more about how you plan to use the gift.

Here is a thank-you note like one you might write:

Dear Aunt Ruth,

Thank you very much for the red scarf you sent for my birthday. It looks very nice with my coat, and I've worn it skating several times. It's warm, too! And I think we are going to have a cold winter, because it has been snowing a lot.

Thank you again.

Love,

Jackie

When your friends or family bring presents to your birthday party, say "thank you" right then and there. Most times, you will not have to write a thank-you note for presents that you receive in person.

Index

Index

A

Abraham 4:134
Absolute zero 1:180
Acceleration 1:93
Aconcagua (mountain) 1:201
Adam's Birthday 4:134
Adams family 3:137
Adams, John 1:236-237, 3:122, 3:129,
  4:112
Adams, John Quincy 1:236-237
Adventures of Tom Sawyer, selection
  4:81-88
Aegean Sea 3:33, 3:39
Aesop 4:10-11
A.F.L. 4:115
Africa 1:10, 1:15; area, 1:195;
  history, 1:204-209; population,
  1:210
Age of Amphibians 2:55
Age of Dinosaurs 2:56
Age of Fishes 2:54
Age of Mammals 2:60-61
Age of Reptiles 2:55-56
Agnew, Spiro 3:188
Air masses 1:36
Air plants 2:81
Airplane, first flight 3:158-162
Alabama 1:238-239
Aladdin and the Magic Lamp 3:60
Alaric 3:53
Alaska 1:238-239

Alaskan brown bear 2:68-69
Alchemy 1:112-116
Aldrin, Edwin 1:47, **3:**184-186
Alexander of Macedon **3:**46
Alexandria, early **3:**54; Lighthouse of,
  1:216
Algae 2:17
Algebra 1:105
Ali Baba and the Forty Thieves 3:60
Alice Meets Humpty Dumpty **4:71-80**
Alice's Adventures in Wonderland,
  selection **4:71-80**
All Hallows Day 4:117
All Saints Day 4:117, 4:148-149
All Souls Day 4:148-149
Allah 3:58
"Allies," in World War I **3:**164
Allosaurus 2:57
Almagest 1:42
Alps Mountains 1:17
Aluminum 1:120
Alveoli 2:144
Amazon River 1:18, 1:196
Amebas 2:63
America, discovery **3:**102-104;
  history, Book 3, *America's Story;* see
  also **United States**
American colonies 3:111, 3:117-120;
  see **United States**
American Federation of Labor
  (A.F.L.) **4:**115
Amino acids 2:133

Ampere **3**:147
Amphibians 2:50; ancient, **2**:55
Analog computer **1**:109
Ancient animals 2:53-61
Andersen, Hans Christian **4**:35-44
Andes mountains, holidays **4**:148
Anemia **2**:136
"Animal Charades" (game) **4**:174
Animal families 2:45-52
Animal Kingdom, chart 2:51
**Animals 2:39-96; ancient, 2:53-61;
biggest, 2:65-69;** changing color,
2:42-43; cold-blooded, **2**:49; desert,
2:87; difference from plants,
2:40-44; forest, **2**:42; tundra, **2**:74;
one-celled, **2**:62; **smallest, 2:62-64;**
warm-blooded, **2**:49; with
backbones, **2**:48-49
Anshan **3**:31
Antarctica **1**:17, **1**:32; area, **1**:195
population, **1**:210
Anthropologist **3**:7
Antibiotics **2**:38
Antietam, battle of **3**:155, **3**:156
Antiochus **4**:131
Apollo **1**:168, **3**:184-186
Apollo XI **1**:47-48
Apothecaries' weights **1**:227
Appalachian Mountains **1**:27
Apple trees **3**:130
Appleseed, Johnny 3:130-132
Aqueducts, Roman **3**:50
Arabia 3:25; ancient, 3:57-60
Arabic numerals 1:103-105, 1:224
Arabs 1;14, **3**:74; **ancient, 3:57-60;**
holy wars, **3**:58
Arachnids **2**:48
Archaeologists **1**:168, **3**:6
Archimedes 1:122-128
Arctic **1**:17; tundra, **2**:72-74
Arctic Ocean **1**:197
Area, measurements of **1**:226
Argentina **1**:18, **1**:199
Aries the Ram (constellation) **1**:40
Aristarchus **1**:42
Aristotle **3**:34, **3**:46
Arithmetic: see Mathematics
Arizona **1**:238-239

Arkansas **1**:238-239
Armstrong, Neil **1**:47, **3**:184-186
Artemis, Temple of **1**:217
Arteries **1**:172; capillary, **2**:142; of
heart, **2**:141
Arthropods 2:47-48
Arthur, Chester A. **1**:236-237
Articles of Confederation **3**:127
Artists, early **3**:22
Asclepius **1**:168
Ash Wednesday **4**:107, **4**:110
Ashura **4**:134
Asia 1:10-12; area, **1**:195; **history,
1:204-209;** population, **1**:210
Asteroids 1:54, 1:60-64
Astronaut: see **Space**
Astronaut party **4**:180
Astronomers **1**:47
Astronomical satellite **1**:84
Astronomy 1:39-70
Aswan Dam **3**:29
Athens, ancient 3:42-46, 3:56
Atlantic Ocean **1**:17, **1**:197
Atmosphere **1**:33, **1**:50
Atom smasher **1**:116
Atomic bomb, first **3**:94, **3**:177
Atomic energy **1**:160
Atomic rays **1**:163
Atomic reactor **1**:160
Atoms 1:159-164; discovery, **1**:115
Atriums (of heart) **2**:140
Attila the Hun **3**:54
Auditory canal **2**:118
Audubon, John James **3**:133
Augustus Caesar **3**:50
Aureomycin **2**:38
Auricle (of ear) **2**:117
Australia 1:24-25; area, **1**:195;
history of, 1:204-209; population,
1:210
Automobile, early American
3:159-160
Autumn parties **4**:162
Avoirdupois measures **1**:227
Awards, Nobel Peace Prize 1:219
Axe, story of **3**:12-14
Axis, of earth **1**:55
Axon **2**:153

B

Babylon, ancient **3**:23-26, **3**:60; defeat
  of, **3**:32; medicine, **1**:167
Bacteria 1:135, **2**:5, **2**:7, **2**:18,
  2:**27-28**, **2**:161
Baghdad **1**:14, **3**:58
"Balance of nature" **2**:70-71
Balloon games **4**:173
Balloons, weather **1**:38
Bamboo tree **2**:33
Banyan tree **2**:32-33
Barbara Frietchie **4**:94-96
Bards **4**:143
Baseball 1:246-250; Little League,
  1:213; Little League champions,
  1:251; World Series champions,
  1:262
Basketball 1:252-257; 1:262
Bastille Day **4**:136
Bath, England **3**:50
Bathing **2**:177
Bathyscaphe *Trieste* **1**:197
Battle of Orleans **4**:136
Battle of Waterloo **3**:88
Bazooka **1**:74
Bear, Kodiak **2**:68-69
Bedouin tribes 3:57-60
Bee **2**:11
Belgium, Christmas in **4**:123
Belshazzar **3**:32
Berbers **3**:60
Bering Sea **1**:198
Behlehem, Jordan **4**:121
Bethlehem, Pennsylvania **4**:125
Bible, printing of **3**:74
Bicentennial **3**:187-190
Biceps **2**:110, **2**:164
Bicycling, safety rules **4**:93
Biggest animals 2:65-69
Biggest plants 2:31-33
Biological clock **1**:182-183
Biologists **2**:8
Biomes **2**:71
Birds 2:50; ancient, **2**:59; smallest,
  2:64
Birth 2:158
Birth defects **1**:178
Birthday of the Prophet **4**:135

"Black Death" **3**:69-70
Blacks **3**:180-183
Blacksmith **3**:114
Bladder **2**:131
Blake, William **4**:91
Blood 2:135-138
Body temperature **1**:225, **2**:150
Bolivar, Simon **4**:149
Bolivia, Incas of **3**:65-68
Bon Matsuri **4**:156
Bonaparte, Napoleon 3:84-88
Bones 2:106-108
Booth, John Wilkes **4**:104
Borneo **1**:24, **1**:196
Botanist **2**:16
Boxing Day **4**:143-144
Boy Scouts of America **1**:212
Boys' Clubs of America **1**:212
Boys' Day **4**:153-154
Boyle, Robert **1**:114, **1**:155
Brady, Mathew 3:154-157
Brahe, Tycho **1**:42
Brahma **4**:159
Brain 2:152-157
Brazil **1**:18; area, **1**:199; Easter in,
  4:109
Breathing **2**:143; **2**:173
Breeds Hill, battle of **3**:120
Bridges, highest **1**:218; longest, **1**:218;
  oldest, **1**:218; world, **1**:218
Brisbane, Australia **1**:25
Bristlecone pine tree **2**:6
British Empire 3:75-79
British Isles 1:22; holidays,
  4:140-143
Bronchial tubes **2**:144
Brontosaurus **2**:56
Brown, Abbie Farwell **4**:19-26
Brownies (Girl Scouts) **1**:212
Brutus **3**:50
Buchanan, James **1**:236-237
Budapest, Hungary **1**:17
Buddhists, holidays of **4**:155
Buildings, largest **1**:217; tallest, **1**:217
Bull dance **3**:40
Bull Run, battle of **3**:155
Bulls, Run of the **4**:138-139
Bulls, sacred **3**:40

Bunker Hill, battle of **3**:120
Buoyancy 1:122-128
Butterfly, dead-leaf **2**:44
"Button, Button" (game) **4**:176

C

Cabinet, United States 1:242
Cactus plants **2**:86
Calculus **1**:105; invention of, **1**:132
California **1**:238-239
Calisthenics **2**:165
Cambodia, cities **3**:22
Cambyses **3**:33
Camels **2**:88-89; in battle, **3**:32
Camp Fire Girls **1**:212
Canada 1:19; area, **1**:199; **holidays,
4:143-144**
Canal, longest ship **1**:217
Candlemaking **3**:114
Candlemas Day **4**:148
Canopus (star) **1**:70
Capacity **1**:227
Cape of Good Hope **3**:100
Capillary arteries **2**:142
Capillary veins **2**:142
"Captain, May I?" (game) **4**:176
Carbohydrates **2**:132
Carbon dioxide **2**:141
Caribbean islands, holidays **4**:145-150
Caribbean Sea **1**:198
Carnival **4**:109
Carnivore **2**:68-69
Carnivorous mammals **2**:52
Carols, Christmas **4**:126
Carroll, Lewis **4**:71-80
Carter, James Earl **1**:236-237
3:187-190
Carthage, ancient **3**:54
Cartilage **2**:106
Cascade Mountains **1**:28
Cat and the Pain-Killer, The **4:81-88**
Cathay **3**:103
Cave men **1**:99-101, **3**:8-9; see also
Early Man
Cave painting **3**:14-16
Cavities **2**:181
Cells 2:7-8, **2:102-104**, **2**:120, **2**:158,
2:160, **4**:8; division, **2**:159

Celsius temperatures **1**:38, **1**:225
Celts, Halloween customs **4**:116
Central America 1:18; **history of,
1:204-209; holidays, 4:145-150**
Centrifugal force **1**:55, **1**:132
Ceppo **4**:125-126
Cerebellum **2**:156
Ceres **4**:121
Chameleon **2**:43-44
"Changing Words" (game) **4**:177
Chapman, John **3**:130-132
Chariot races **3**:51
**Chemistry 1:117-121; history of,
1:112-116**
Cheops, Pharaoh **3**:28
Chicken pox **2**:162
Child's Garden of Verses, A, selections
4:90
Childbirth, **2**:158
Children's Day **4**:155
Ch'in Dynasty **3**:36
China 1:12; area, **1**:199; **Great Wall
of, 3:34-36; holidays, 4:150-153;**
New Year's, **4**:100; plague, **3**:70;
population, **1**:210; rivers, **3**:22
Chinese numerals **1**:224
Ching Chi **4**:153
Ching Ming **4**:153
Chlorella **2**:28
Chlorination **1**:121
Chlorophyll **2**:10
**Christian holidays; see Christmas,
Easter,** and names of countries
Christians, in India **4**:157
Christmas 4:121-127; carols, **4**:126;
parties, **4**:184; trees, **4**:123
Chromosomes **2**:158
Church of England **3**:108
Cilia **2**:63
Cinchona tree **2**:37
Cinco de Mayo **4**:150
C.I.O. **4**:115
Circulatory system 2:142
Circus party **4**:181
Cirrus clouds **1**:34
Cities, ancient 3:19-22
Cities, largest in United States, **1**:210;
largest in world, **1**:210

City-states, Greece **3**:42
Civil rights movement 3:180-183,
nonviolence **3**:188-190; riots **3**:190;
see also **Minority Groups**
Civil War, United States 3:151-153,
3:154-157, 4:104, 4:111
Civil War states 1:235
Clark, William **3**:129
Cleanliness **2**:177
Clermont **3**:142
Cleveland, Grover **1**:236-237, **4**:115
Clouds 1:33-34
Coal **2**:26
Coal Age **2**:26
Coccyx **2**:108
Cochlea **2**:118
Cocullo, Italy **4**:139
Code Napoleon **3**:85
Coelenterata **2**:46
Coins and currency, foreign 1:229;
United States, 1:228
Colon **2**:130
Colonial life 3:112-114
Colorado **1**:27, **1**:238-239
Colorado River **1**:30
Colossus of Rhodes **1**:216
Columbus, Christopher 3:102-104
Columbus Day **3**:104
Combustion chamber **1**:78
Comets 1:54, 1:60-62
Committees of Correspondence **3**:116
Common Sense **4**:112
Commonwealth Day **4**:141
Communications satellite **1**:83
Communists, North Korean **3**:182
Composite group (flowering plants)
2:20-22
Computers 1:106-111
Conception **2**:159
Concord, Mass. **4**:112; battle, **3**:117,
3:119
Condensation **1**:34
Conduction **1**:143
Cones, of plants **2**:20
Confederate States of America **3**:152;
list of, **1**:235
Congress, U.S. 1:243; representatives
per state, **1**:238-241

Congress of Industrial Organizations
(C.I.O.) **4**:115
Congreve, William **1**:72
Coniferous forests 2:75-77
Conifers (plants) **2**:26
Connecticut **1**:238-239
Constantine **4**:107
Constantinople **3**:51
Constellations **1**:40
Constitution, United States 3:127-128
Constitution Day, Japan **4**:156-157;
Norway, **4**:139
Continental Congress **3**:121, **3**:127
Continental drift **1**:10
Continents 1:10; 1:12-20; area, **1**:195
Convection **1**:144
Coolidge, Calvin **1**:236-237
Copernicus, Nicolas **1**:42, **1**:53, **1**:55,
3:73
Cordova, Spain **3**:60
Cords, vocal **2**:145
Corn, in early America **3**:109-111
Cornea **2**:115
Cornwallis, General Charles **3**:125,
3:126, **4**:113
Corpus Christi Day **4**:139, **4**:145-146
Corpuscles **2**:135-136
Cortex **2**:155
Cortisone **2**:37
Cos (island) **1**:170
Costumes, party 4:179-185
Cotton **3**:26, **3**:146
Cotton plantation **3**:146
Counterforce **1**:78
Counting, ancient methods 1:99-105
Countries, largest **1**:199; smallest,
1:199
Cranium **2**:106
Creche (Christmas) **4**:123
Creosote plant **2**:86
Crete, ancient 3:37-40
Croesus **3**:31-32
Cro-Magnon man **3**:14-16
Crusades **3**:74
Crust, of earth **1**:10
Crustaceans 2:48
Cyrogenics 1:179-181
Cub Scouts **1**:212

Cumulus clouds 1:34
Curare 2:35-37
Currency, foreign 1:229; United States, 1:228
Cycads (plants) 2:26
Cyclotron 1:116
Cyrus the Great 3:30-32
Cytoplasm 2:104
Czar, of Russia 3:80
Czechoslovakia 1:17

D

Daedalus 1:44
Dalton, John 1:116
Damascus, Syria 1:14
Dams, largest 1:218; tallest, 1:218
Danish Fairy Tales and Legends, selection **4:35-44**
Darius 3:33
Dark Ages 3:52-56, 3:89; beginning, 3:51; end, 3:69-71
Dark nebula 1:68
David 4:134
Da Vinci, Leonardo 3:71-72
Davis, Jefferson 3:152
Day of Atonement 4:130
Day of the Holy Cross 4:147-148
Day of the Three Kings 4:127
Dead-leaf butterfly 2:44
Deceleration 1:93
Deciduous forest 2:75-78
Declaration of Independence 3:121-123, 4:112; **signers of, 1:234**
Decoration Day 4:111
Decorations, party 4:179-185
DeGraaf, Regnier 1:137
Delaware 1:238-239
Delft, Netherlands 1:135
Delta, river 1:31
Demeter 4:121
Democracy, Greek 3:41-46
Dendrites 2:153
Denmark 1:16; holidays, 4:139-140; Vikings, 3:61-64
Dentine 2:128
Dentistry 1:176
Dermis 2:150

Desalination 1:160
Desert animals 2:87
Desert tortoise 2:88
Deserts 1:197, 2:85-89
Dia de la Cruz 4:147
Diaphragm 2:146
Diet, proper 2:132
Digestive system 2:127-128; digestion, 2:128
Digital computer 1:109
Digitalis 2:37
Dingo 1:24
Dinichtys 2:54-55
Dinosaurs 2:56-60
Diplodocus 2:56-57
Diphtheria 2:163
Diseases 2:162; see also **Medicine**
Displacement of water 1:124
Divali 4:158
Dominion Day, Canada 4:143
Dorchester Heights, battle 3:120
Double star 1:68
Douglas, Stephen 4:103
Drake, Sir Francis 3:79
Dreidel games 4:131
Drugs 1:174; miracle, 1:121; see also **Medicine**
Druids 4:117
Dry measures 1:227
Dublin, Ireland 4:142
Duck-billed platypus 1:24
Durga Puja 4:159

E

Eardrums 2:117
Early man, first cities, 3:19-22; hunting, 3:17; **mathematics, 1:99-101;** medicine 1:165-166; **myths and religion, 1:39-42,** 3:19-20; **villages, 3:17-18**
Ears 2:117-118
Earth 1:5-38, 1:56-57; atmosphere, 1:33; center, 1:28; composition, 1:8-10; crust, 1:10; early, 1:8-10; **facts about, 1:193-201; geology and geography, 1:8-32;** population, 1:210
Earthquakes 1:9, 1:28

East Roman Empire **3**:51
Easter 4:107-110; in Italy, **4**:139; parade, **4**:107; parties, **4**:185
Easter eggs **4**:108
Echinodermata **2**:46
Eclipse, lunar **1**:52; solar, **1**:52
Ecology 2:70-96
Edison, Thomas **1**:121
Egg, human **2**:158
Egypt 4:133; **ancient, 3:27-29;** mathematics, **1**:101; medicine, **1**:167; pyramids, **1**:216, **3**:27-29
Egyptian numerals **1**:224
Eisenhower, Dwight D. **1**:236-237, **3**:180-183
Eisteddfod **4**:143
Elbrus (mountain) **1**:201
Electric computer, first **1**:108
Elephant, African **2**:67
Elizabeth I, Queen 3:75-79
Ellipse **1**:54, **1**:60
Emancipation Proclamation **3**:153, **4**:104
Embryo **2**:160
Embryophyta 2:17-22
Emperor, Roman **3**:49
Empire Day **4**:141
Enamel, of teeth **2**:128
England 1:22, **3:75-79;** Christmas, **4**:126; Easter, **4**:108, **4**:110; Halloween, **4**:118; **holidays, 4:140-143;** New Year's, **4**:100
English Channel **3:**79, **3:**86
Enterprize **3**:185
Entertaining 4:161-190
Eohippus **2**:60
Epidermis **2**:150
Equality: see **Civil Rights Movement**
Erik the Red **3**:63
Eros (asteroid) **1**:64
Erosion of land **1**:31
Eryops **2**:55
Eskimos **1:**19, **3:**64
Esophagus **2**:128
Esther, Book of **4**:130
Etruscans **3:**47, **3:**49
Euphrates River, cities of **3**:21
Europe 1:10, **1:15-16;** area, **1**:195;

history (time line), **1:204-209; holidays, 4:136-140;** plague, **3:**70; population, **1**:210
Evaporation **1**:34
Events, historical (time line) **1:204-209**
Everest, Mt. **1**:201
Evergreens **2**:77
Evolution **3**:8
Exercise 2:165-168
Exodus, Book of **4**:132-133
Exploration, early 3:99-104
Exploration of space 1:17, **1:81-84;** see also **Space**
Explorer I **1**:81
Exponent **1**:105
Eyes 2:114-116

F

Fahrenheit temperature **1:**38, **1:**225
Fairy Tales from Grimm, selection **4:28-34**
Fat **2**:132
Fatigue **2**:175
Fawkes, Guy **4**:141
Feast of Booths **4**:121
Feast of Lanterns **4**:151
Feast of Light **4**:130
Feast of Tabernacles **4**:121
Fermentation **2**:30
Fertilization **2**:159
Fertilizers, chemical **1**:117
Festival of Lanterns **4**:156
Festival of Tools **4**:159
Fetus **2**:160
Feudalism 3:55-56
Field, Eugene **4**:92-93
Fillmore, Millard **1**:236-237
Fingerprints **2**:150
Finland 1:16; **holidays, 4:139-140**
Fiords **1**:16
Fireballs **1**:62
First aid **2**:185
Fish 2:49; fresh water, **2:**90-92; salt water, **2:**93-96

Flatboat **3**:145

Flatworms **2**:46-47

Fleming, Dr. Alexander **1**:174

Flint **3**:13

Floating plants **2**:92

Florida **1**:238-239

Flowering plants **2**:20

Flowers, of plants **2**:11

Fluid tissue **2**:135

Fluidics 1:182

Fluoride **1**:116

Follicles **2**:150

Foods, basic **2**:134; elements of,
  2:132; **party, 4:168-170**

Football 1:258-262

Ford, Gerald **1**:236-237, **3**:188-190

Ford, Henry **3**:159

Ford's Theater **4**:104

Forest 2:75-81; coniferous, **2**:75-77;
  deciduous, **2**:75-78; tropical rain,
  2:78-81

Forest canopy **2**:78, **2**:80

Fort Sumter **3**:153, **3**:154

Fossils **2**:23, **2**:53-54

Four-H Clubs **1**:212

Fourth of July: see **Independence
  Day**

France 1:16; Christmas, **4**:125, **4**:127;
  holidays, 4:136-137; New Year's,
  4:100

Frankincense **4**:127

Franklin, Benjamin 3:115-116, 3:122,
  3:147, **4**:112

French Revolution **3**:85, **4**:136

Fresh water communities 2:90-92

Friction **1**:141

Frog Prince, The **4:28-34**

Frontier life 3:133-136

Frozen sleep **1**:181

Fuel, rocket **1**:72, **1**:78

Fulton, Robert 3:140-142

"Fulton's Folly" **3**:142

Fungi **2**:18; importance of, **2**:30

G

**Galaxy, Milky Way 1:40, 1:66-67,
  1:**87

Galen 1:171-172

Galleon, Spanish **3**:76, **3**:78

Games, party 4:171-177

Ganges River, cities of **3**:22

Garfield, James A. **1**:236-237

Gas, helium **1**:46

Gaseous nebula **1**:68

Gaucho **1**:18

Gaul, invasion of **3**:49

Geiger counter **1**:160

Gemini Twins (constellation) **1**:68

Geography 1:12-25

Geology 1:26-32; creation of
  continents, **1**:8-10

Geometry **1**:105

Georgia **1**:238-239

German tribes, ancient **3**:51

Germany 1:16, **3:92; after World War
  I, 3**:92, **3:163-166;** ancient, **3**:52;
  Christmas, **4**:123; Easter, **4**:108,
  4:110; **holidays, 4**:137; union of,
  3:90; **World War II, 3:92-95, 3:176**

Germs **2**:137, **2**:161

Gettysburg, battle of **3**:157

Giraffe **2**:68

Girls' Clubs of America **1**:212

Girl Scouts of the U.S.A. **1**:212

Glaciers 1:26-32, 3:10

Glands, sweat **2**:149

Glassmaker **3**:114

Glaucoma **2**:37

Glider, early **3**:158-162

Gobi Desert **1**:197

Goddard, Dr. Robert H. 1:71-73

Godwin-Austen (mountain) **1**:201

Gompers, Samuel **4**:115

Good Friday **4**:107, **4**:109, **4**:110

Goths 3:52-56

Gourd family **2**:22

Grand Canyon **1**:30

Grant, Ulysses S. **1**:236-237, **3**:157

Grass family **2**:22

Grassland 2:82-84

Gravity 1:55, **1**:61, **1:129-134;** loss of,
  1:83

Great Arabian Desert **1**:197

Great Australian Desert **1**:197

Great Britain 3:75-79; holidays,
  4:140-143

Great Lakes **1**:32, **1**:198
Great Wall of China 3:34-36, 3:52
Greece, ancient 3:41-46; mathematics,
  1:102; Thanksgiving celebration,
  4:121
Greek numerals **1**:224
Greenland **1**:196; discovery of, **3**:63
Grimm, Jacob and Wilhelm **4**:28-34
Grooming, proper 2:177
Groundhog Day **4**:148
Guest, being a 4:186-189; greeting,
  4:164
Guillotine **3**:85
Gulf of Chihli **3**:34
Gunpowder **3**:74
Gunpowder Plot **4**:141
Guy Fawkes Day **4**:141

H

Haggadah **4**:133
Haggis **4**:142
Hair, care of **2**:178
Halicarnassus, tomb at **1**:216
Halley, Edmund **1**:42, **1**:62
Halley's Comet **1**:62
Halloween 4:116-119; parties, **4**:184
Hamamatsu, Japan **4**:155
Haman **4**:130
Hamilton, Alexander **3**:128
Hammurabi **1**:167, **3**:26
Hancock, John **4**:112
Hanging Gardens of Babylon 1:216,
  3:26, 3:56
Hanukkah 4:130-131
Harding, Warren G. **1**:236-237
Harrison, Benjamin **1**:236-237
Harrison, William H. **1**:236-237
Hawaii **1**:22, **1**:24, **1**:238-239
Hawthorne, Nathaniel **4**:13-18
Hayes, Rutherford B. **1**:236-237
Healing plants 2:34-39
Health, rules of 2:173
Hearing 2:117
Heart 1:176, **2**:113, **2:139-141**
Heartbeat **2**:140
Heat 1:141-146
Hebrews, early mathematics **1**:102;
  see also **Jewish holidays**

Helium gas **1**:46
Hemispheres, of cortex **2**:155
Hemoglobin **2**:136
Henry, Patrick **3**:122
Herbivores **2**:68
Herbivorous mammals **2**:52
Herculaneum **1**:29
Hey! Diddle Diddle **4**:6
Hibernation of animals **2**:41-42
Hickory, Dickory Dock **4**:7
Hidalgo, Miguel **4**:149
Hiero, king of Syracuse **1**:123
Hieroglyphics **1**:168
Himalaya Mountains **1**:10; **1**:201
Hina Matsuri **4**:153
Hindu-Arabic numerals 1:103-105,
  1:224
Hindu numerals **1**:224
Hippocrates 1:168-171
Hippocratic oath **1**:170
Hiroshima, Japan **4**:157
History of the world (time line)
  1:204-209
Hitler, Adolf 3:92-95, 3:174, **3:**177
"Hockey, Balloon" (game) **4**:173
Hokkaido (island) **1**:22
Holi **4**:158
Holidays, American 4:99-127; world,
  4:128-159
Holland, Christmas in **4**:123
Holly **4**:125
Holy Eucharist **4**:139
Holy Week **4**:108; in Italy, **4**:139; in
  Spain, **4**:138
Hong Kong **1**:22
Honshu (island) **1**:22
Hooke, Robert **1**:138-139
Hoover, Herbert **1**:236-237
Horseless carriage **3**:159
Host and hostess, party 4:163-165
"Hot and Cold" (game) **4**:176
House of Lords **4**:140, **4**:141
House of Representatives, U.S.
  1:243
Houses, colonial **3**:112
Human body 2:99-104
Humidity **1**:38
Hummingbird **2**:64

Hungary **1**:17
Huns 3:51, **3:52-56, 3**:74
Hurricane **1**:37
Hussein **4**:134-135
Hydrogen **1**:46; in water molecule,
  1:116

I

Icarus **1**:44
Ice Age 1:31-32
Iceland, settling of **3**:63
Icelandic poems **3**:64
Idaho **1**:238-239
If **4**:7
Illinois **1**:238-239
"I'm Taking a Trip" (game) **4**:177
Imhotep **1**:167
Immunity **2**:163
In the Days of Giants, selection **4:19-26**
Incas 3:65-68
Independence Day (July 4th) 3:123,
  4:112-114, 4:149
Independence Day, in India **4**:157; in
  Latin America, **4**:149-150
India 1:10, **1**:13; area, **1**:199;
  holidays, 4:157-159; population,
  1:210
Indian Ocean **1**:197
Indiana **1**:197
Indiana **1**:238-239
Indians, American 1:232-233;
  Columbus and, **3**:103; at
  Jamestown, **3**:106
Indonesia **1**:28
Indus River **3**:33
Infrared light **1**:151
Insects 2:47-48
Intercontinental ballistic missiles
  (ICBM) **1**:75
International Labor Day, in U.S.S.R.
  4:140
Intestines **2**:129-130
Introductions **4**:164
Inventions, table of 1:185-190
Inventors 1:185-190
Invertebrates **2**:45
Invincible Armada 3:75-79
Invitations, party 4:163-164, 4:167

Involuntary muscles **2**:112
Iowa **1**:238-239
Iran **1**:14, **4**:133
Iraq **1**:14
Ireland 1:22; Halloween, **4**:117-118;
  holidays, 4:140-143
Iris (of eye) **2**:115
Isabella, Queen **3**:103
Ishmael **4**:134
Islam 3:58; holidays, **4:133-135**
Island Kingdom (Crete) **3:37-40**
Islands 1:21-25; largest, 1:196
Isometrics **2**:168
Isotonics 2:168
Israel 1:14, **4**:129
Italy, Christmas in **4**:125-126; Easter
  in, **4**:109; **holidays, 4:139;** invasion
  by Goths, **3**:52; union of, **3**:91

J

Jack-o-lanterns **4**:118
Jackson, Andrew 3:137-139, 3:153,
  1:236-237
Jains **4**:157
Jamestown, Va., **3**:105-107
Japan 1:13, **1**:22; in World War II,
  3:93-95, **3**:174-176; **holidays,
  4:153-157;** New Year's, **4**:101;
  surrender of **3**:177-179
Java **1**:24
Jefferson, Thomas 1:236-237,
  3:121-123, **3**:128, **4**:112
Jesus Christ, birth of **4**:121
Jewish holidays 4:129-132
Jews, Thanksgiving celebration **4**:121
Joan of Arc, Feast of **4**:136-137
Johnny Appleseed 3:130-132
Johnson, Andrew **1**:236-237
Johnson, Lyndon B. **1**:236-237
Joints **2**:106
Joseph **4**:121, **4**:134
Judas Iscariot **4**:109
Judas Maccabeus **4**:131
Judicial Departments (U.S.
  government) **1**:243
Julius Caesar 3:49-50
Jungle **2**:78
Jungle Book, The, selection **4:46-54**

Jupiter **1**:57; moons of, **1**:48

K

Kaiser, of Germany **3**:92, **3**:164
Kalahari Desert **1**:197
Kanchenjunga (mountain) **1**:201
Kangaroo **1**:24
Kansas **1**:238-239
Kara Kum Desert **1**:197
Kelp **2**:33
Kennedy, John Fitzgerald 3:180-183,
 1:236-237
Kentucky **1**:238-239
Kepler, Johann **1**:42
Khufu (Cheops) **3**:28
Kidneys, **2**:131; transplant, **1**:176
Kilimanjaro (mountain) **1**:201
"King-bull" **3**:40
King, Dr. Martin Luther 3:180-183
King James of England **3**:105
"King Momus" **4**:101
King Philip of Spain **3**:76-77
Kipling, Rudyard **4**:46-54
"Kitchen God" **4**:151
Kitty Hawk, N.C. **3**:159-162
Knights of Labor **4**:115
Koala **1**:24
Kodiak bear **2**:68-69
Kol Nidre **4**:130
Kombé poison **2**:37
Koran **4**:133
Kosciusko (mountain) **1**:201
Krakatoa (mountain) **1**:28
Kremlin **3**:82
Krill **2**:66-67
Kris Kringle **4**:122
Kyushu (island) **1:22**
Kyzyl Kum Desert **1**:197

L

Labor Day 4:114
Labor unions **4**:115
Lake Erie **1**:198
Lake Huron **1**:198
Lake Michigan **1**:198
Lake Ontario **1**:198
Lake Superior **1**:198
Lakshmi **4**:158

Land areas, lowest 1:201
Languages, most widely spoken 1:211
Laos, cities of **3**:22
Larynx **2**:145
Laser ray 1:153
Last Supper, The **3**:71
Latin America, Easter in, **4**:108;
 holidays, **4:145-150;** see also **South**
 America
Latin, language **3**:49
Latins, ancient **3**:47, **3**:49
Lava **1**:28
Law of Universal Gravitation **1**:134
Laws, early **3**:25; Roman, **3**:50
League of Nations 3:96, 3:164-166
Leaves **2**:12-13
Lebanon **3**:25
Lee, Robert E. **4**:157
Leeuwenhoek, Anton von 1:135-140
Legends 4:12-26
Legislative branch (U.S. government)
 1:243-244
Leif Erikson **3**:63
Length **1**:226
Leningrad, U.S.S.R. **3**:83
Lens (of eye) **2**:115
Lent **4**:107, **4**:109, **4**:110
Leonardo da Vinci 3:71-72
Levers 1:127-128
Lewis and Clark expedition **3**:129
Lewis, Meriwether **3**:129
Lexington, battle of **3**:118, **4**:112
Lhotse (mountain) **1**:201
Li Chum **4**:152
Libyan Desert **1**:197
Lichen **2**:18; in tundra, **2**:73-74
Liechtenstein, area of **1**:199
Ligaments **2**:106
Light 1:148-153; speed of, **1**:66,
 1:152, **1**:157
Lighthouse of Alexandria **1**:216
Light waves **1**:151, **2**:115
Light year **1**:67
Lily family **2**:22
Lincoln, Abraham 1:236-237,
 3:151-153, 4:120
Lincoln's Birthday 4:102-104; parties,
 4:183

Lindbergh, Charles **3:**167-170
Liquid measures **1:**227
"Little Corporal, The" 3:84-88
Little League Baseball **1:**212
Liver **2:**129
Liverworts **2:**19
Living things, general description
  2:5-8
Livingston, Robert **3:**142
Llama **3:**66, **3:**67, **3:**68
Local winds **1:**36
Lockjaw **2:**163
Logan, General John A. **4:**111
Long Island, N.Y,. **1:**21
Louisiana **1:**238-239
Louisiana Purchase **3:**129
"Lucky Lindy" **3:**167-170
Lumination **1:**149
Luna XIV **1:**47
Lunar eclipse **1:**52
Lunar year **4:**150
Lungs **2:**144
Lunokhod **1:**47-48
Luther, Martin **4:**123
Lydia (country) **3:**31-32

M

MacArthur, General Douglas **3:**177
Maccabees **4:**131
Maccabeus, Judas **4:**131
Macedonians **3:**46
McKinley, William **1:**236-237
Madagascar **1:**196
Madison, James **1:**236-237
Magi **4:**122
Magnifying glass **1:**135-140
Maine **1:**238-239
Makalu (mountain) **1:**201
Malaria **2:**37
Malay Sea **1:**198
Mammals 2:52; ancient, **2:**60-61
Mammoths **2:**60, **3:**11
Man, accomplishments of 1:215;
  Cro-Magnon, **3:**14-16; **early, 3:**5-9;
  evolution of, **3:**8; **history of,**
  1:204-209; **modern, 3:**14-16;
  Neanderthal, **3:**14; races, **3:**16
Man, the Boy and the Donkey, The

4:10-11
Manchuria **3:**34
Mandible **2:**106
Manhattan Island, N.Y. **1:**21
Manners 4:186-190
Mardi Gras **4:**110
Marie Antoinette **3:**85
Mariner IX **1:**83
Marrow **2:**108
Mars 1:57
Mary (mother of Jesus) **4:**121
Maryland **1:**238-239
Massachusetts Bay Colony **3:**111
Mastodons **2:**60
Mathematics 1:99-111; history,
  1:99-105; kinds of numerals, **1:**224
Matzoh **4:**133
May Day **4:**139
Mayflower **3:**108-109, **4:**119
Mayflower Compact **3:**109
Mayfly **2:**6
Measles **2:**163
Measures and Weights 1:226-227
Medes, defeat of **3:**31
Medicine 1:165-178; ancient,
  1:165-172; dangers of, **2:**184;
  healing plants, **2:**34-39; history,
  1:165-172; modern, 1:**173-178;
  preventive, **1:**176; space, **1:**184
"Medicine man" **1:**165-166, **2:**34
Mediterranean Sea **1:**198, **3:**37
Medulla **2:**157
Melanesia **1:**24
Melanocytes **2:**149
Melbourne, Australia **1:**25
Membrane **2:**103
Memorial Day 4:110-112
Menorah **4:**131
Merchants, early **3:**22
Mercury 1:55-56
Merry Adventures of Robin Hood, The,
  selection **4:**55-64
Mesopotamia, mathematics of 1:101
Messiah **4:**122
Meteor 1:54, **1:**60-64
Meteorite **1:**62
Meteorological satellite **1:**83
Meteorology: see **Weather**

Metric system **1:226-227**
Mexico 1:19; Christmas, 4:125; Easter, 4:108; **holidays, 4:145-150;** Independence Day, 4:149; St. John's Day, 4:147
Michigan 1:238-239
Microbes 1:135-140, 2:27-28
Microbiology 1:139
Micronesia 1:24
Microscope 1:137-140
Middle East 1:14; **Arab tribes, 3:57-60; history, 1:204-209**
"Midnight Sun" 1:16
Midsummer's Eve 4:139, 4:146-147
Migration of animals 2:41
Milan, Italy 3:54
Milky Way galaxy 1:40, **1:60-67,** 1:87
Minerals 2:133
Minnesota 1:238-239
Minority groups 3:180-183
Minotaur 3:40
Minutemen 3:118-120, 4:112
Miracle drugs 1:121
Missiles 1:48, **1:71-80,** 1:75
Mississippi (state) 1:238-239
Mississippi river 1:31, 3:143-146
Mississippi-Missouri-Red Rock river, 1:196
Mississippi Steamboat 3:143-146
Missouri (state) 1:238-239
Missouri, U.S.S. 3:180
Mistletoe 4:125
Mohammed 3:58; see also **Moslems**
Mohammedans 4:133; see also **Moslems**
Molds 2:30
"Molecular theory of heat" 1:143
Molecule 1:116, 1:141-143
Mollusks 2:47
Molting 2:48
Mona Lisa 3:71
Monaco, area of 1:199
Money 1:228-229
Mongolia 3:34
Mongols 3:16, 3:35, 3:52, 3:74
Monroe, James 1:236-237
Montana 1:27, 1:240-241
Moon 1:47-52, 1:54; composition of,
1:50; distance, 1:49; eclipse, 1:52; landing, 1:47-48
Moors 3:60, 3:74
Morse Code 3:147-150
Morse, Samuel 3:147-150
Moscow, U.S.S.R. 3:82
Moses 4:132, 4:134
Moslem Empire 3:58; see also **Arabs**
Moslem holidays 4:133-134
Moslems, early 3:58; holidays, **4:133-134;** in India, 4:157
Mosques 3:60, 4:133
Moss 2:19-20
Mount Everest 1:201
Mount McKinley 1:201
Mount Olympus 3:43
Mount Vernon 4:106
Mount Vesuvius 1:29
Mountains, age of 1:27; **highest, 1:201**
Mowgli's Brothers 4:46-54
Muharram 4:134
"Mummers parade" 4:101
Mumps 2:162
Munich Oktoberfest 4:137
Muscles 2:109-112; exercising, 2:164-169
Muscular dystrophy 2:37
"Musical Chairs" (game) 4:175
Mussolini, Benito 3:93
Myrrh 4:127

N

Napoleon Bonaparte 3:84-88
Napoleonic Wars 1:72, 3:84-88
Nations, largest 1:210
Nativity scenes 4:123
Natural communities of plants and animals 2:70-72
Navels 2:160
Nazi Party 3:176; see also **Hitler, Adolf**
Neanderthal man 3:14
Nebraska 1:240-241
Nebula 1:68
Negev Desert 3:25

Neptune 1:58-59
Nerves 2:153-155
Nervous system 2:157
Neurons 2:153
Neva River 3:83
Nevada 1:240-241
"New Deal" 3:171
New England, settling of 3:109
New Guinea 1:22, 1:196
New Hampshire 1:240-241
New Jersey 1:240-241
New Mexico 1:240-241
New Orleans, La. 4:110
New Orleans (steamboat) 3:143
New Year, Chinese, 4:150; Jewish,
    4:130; Moslem, 4:134; United
    States, 4:99-102
New York (state) 1:240-241
New York City 1:21
Newton, Sir Isaac 1:42, 1:55,
    1:129-134, 1:150, 1:151
Niacin 2:133
Night Before Christmas, The 4:123
Nightingale, The 4:35-44
Nightshade family 2:22
Nile River 1:196; cities of, 3:21;
    valley, 3:27-28
Nina (ship) 3:103
Nixon, Richard M. 1:231, 3:188
Noah's Ark 4:134
Nobel Peace Prize winners 1:219
Normandy 3:63
North America 1:10, 1:19-20; area,
    1:195; history of, 1:204-209;
    population, 1:116
North Carolina 1:240-241
North Dakota 1:240-241
North Pole 1:32
North Star 1:42
Norway 1:16; Christmas in, 4:123;
    Constitution Day, 4:139;
    holidays, 4:139-140;
    Vikings, 3:61-64
Nose 2:122-123
Nourishment, proper 2:132
Nubian Desert 1:197
Numbers 1:99-111, 1:223-229; see
    also Mathematics

Numerals 1:223-229; see also
    Mathematics
Nutrition 2:132
Nylon 1:120

O

Ob-Irtish River 1:196
Oceania 1:22-24
Oceans 1:8; ancient, 1:8-10; islands
    in, 1:21-25; sizes of 1:197; and
    weather, 1:34-36
Odometer 1:109
Ohio 1:240-241
Oklahoma 1:240-241
Oktoberfest 4:137
"Old Hickory" 3:137-139
Old Mother Hubbard 4:8-9
Olfactory membrane 2:123
Olympic Games 3:43
Oregon 1:240-241
Organizations for Young People
    1:212-213
Orleans, battle of 4:136
Organism 2:161
Organs 2:104
Ostrich 2:69
O'Sullivan, Tim 3:155
Ottawa, Canada 4:143
Outer Space 1:5; early ideas about,
    1:39-42; life in, 1:86-92; travel in,
    1:93-96; see also Space
Ovum 2:158
Oxidizer 1:78
Oxygen, discovery of 1:115; in blood,
    2:136

P

Pacific Ocean 1:22-24; 1:197
Padi 1:12
Paine, Thomas 4:112
Pakistan 4:133; population, 1:210
Paleontologist 3:6
Palm Sunday 4:109; see also Easter
Pampas 1:18, 2:82
Pamplona, Spain 4:138
Panama, holidays in 4:145
Panama Canal 1:19
Pancreas 2:129

Pangaea **1**:9
Paper, invention of **3**:74
Paraguay, St. John's Day in **4**:147
Paramecium **2**:63
Parasites **2**:62
Parties 4:161-190; occasions for,
    4:161-162; planning, **4**:163
Pasos **4**:138
Passion plays **4**:109
Passover **4**:131-132
Patriotic holidays, parties for **4**:183;
    see also **Holidays, American**
Pea family **2**:22
Peace Festival **4**:157
Peach Blossom Festival **4**:153
Pearl Harbor 3:94, 3:174-176
Peat moss **2**:37-38
Pen Pals, World **1**:213
Pencil-and-paper games **4**:177
Penicillin **1**:121, **2**:30, **2**:38; discovery
    of, **1**:174
Peninsulas **1**:16
Pennsylvania **1**:240-241
People and their ways 1:203-213
Peristalsis **2**:130
Persia, ancient 3:30-33
Perspiration **2**:150
Peru, Christmas in **4**:127; holidays,
    4:145; **Incas of, 3:65-68;**
    Independence Day, **4**:150
Peter the Great 3:80-83
Petrified Forest National Monument
    2:24
Pharaohs of Egypt **3**:28
Philistines **3**:40
Philosophers, Greek **3**:45
Phlogiston **1**:114
Photography, early American **3**:155
Photons **1**:151
Photosynthesis **2**:10
Phylum **2**:20
Physical fitness 2:164-172; health
    rules, 2:173-176
Piccard, Dr. Jacques **1**:197
Pierce, Franklin **1**:197
Pierce, Franklin **1**:236-237
Pigmy shrew **2**:64
Pilgrims 3:108-111; Thanksgiving,
    4:119-120
"Pin the Tail" (game) **4**:172
Piñata **4**:125
Pinocchio **4:19-27**
Pinta **3**:103
Pinus ponderosa **2**:16
Pioneer life in America 3:133-136
"Pirates," English **3**:76
Pisces the Fish (constellation)
    1:40-41
Placenta **2**:160
Plague **3**:69
Planetary nebula **1**:68
Planets 1:5, 1:53-59
Plankton 2:66-67, 2:92, 2:94
Plant families 2:16-22
Plant Kingdom 2:8; chart of, 2:21
Plants 2:8-38; air, **2**:81; **ancient,**
    2:23-26; biggest, 2:31-33; cactus,
    2:86; **difference from animals,**
    2:40-44; floating, **2**:92; flowers of,
    2:11; fossil, **2**:23; scientific names
    of, **2**:16-17; **smallest, 2:27-28**
Plasma (blood) **2**:135
Plasma (matter) **1**:181
Platelet **2**:136
Plato **3**:45
Platypus **1**:24
Pleiades **1**:68
Plesiosaur **2**:57
Pluto 1:54, 1:59
Pocahontas **3**:106, **3**:107
Poisons, dangers of **2**:184
Poland **1**:17; Christmas in, **4**:126
Polar wind **1**:35
Polaris **1**:42
Pole Star **1**:42
Polio **2**:163; polio vaccine, **1**:176
Polk, James K. **1**:236-237
Pollen **2**:11
Polo, Marco **3**:99, **3**:103
Polynesia **1**:24
Pompeii **1**:29
Populations 1:210
Portugal, sailors from **3**:99-101; **3**:102
Posture 2:176-181
Potomac River **4**:106
Powhatan **3**:106

Prague, Czech. **1**:17
Prairie 2:82-84
Prehistoric man: see **Early Man**
**Presidents of the United States
1:236-237**
Pressure suit **1**:93
Prevailing winds **1**:35-36; easterlies
and westerlies, **1**:35
Primates, study of **3:7**
Primitive man: see **Early Man**
Prince Henry of Portugal 3:99-101
Princeton, battle of **3**:126
Principia **1**:130
Printing press invention of **3**:74
Prism **1**:132, **1**:150
"Promised land" **4**:132
Prontosil **1**:174
Prophet, Birthday of **4**:135
Protein **2**:133
Protista **2**:8
Protoplasm **2**:104
Protozoa 2:5, 2:45, 2:62-63, 2:92
Prussia **3**:90
Psilopsid plants **2**:24-25
Pterodactyls **2**:59
Ptolemy **1**:42
Pupil (of eye) **2**:115
Pure and Bright Festival **4**:153
Purim **4**:130
Puritans **3**:108
Pyle, Howard **4**:55-64
**Pyramids of Egypt 1:216, 3:28-29,
3:56**

Q
Queen Elizabeth I 3:75-79
Queen Isabella **3**:103
Quinine **2**:37

R
Races of man **3**:16
Radar **1**:153
Radiation **1**:145
Radio astronomy **1**:91-91, **1**:184
Radioactive atoms **1**:163
Radioisotopes 1:160-163
Rain **1**:33
Rain, Rain, Go Away **4:7**

Rainbow **1**:150
Rainfall, greatest **1**:200
Rain forests 2:78-81
Ramadan **4**:133
Rapunzel **4:65-73**
Reagan, Ronald W. **3**:190
Redwood trees **2**:31
Reflection **1**:149
Reflex action **2**:155
Relative humidity **1**:38
"Relay, Balloon" (game) **4**:173
Remus **3**:49
Renaissance 3:69-74
Reproduction 2:7, 2:158-160
Reptiles 2:50; ancient 2:53-60
Republic Day **4**:157
Respiratory system 2:143-146
Rest, proper **2**:175
Retina **2**:116
Revere, Paul **3**:117, **4**:112
Revolution, French **3**:85, **4**:136
Revolution, Russian **4**:140
**Revolutionary War, American
3:124-126, 4:105**
Rhode Island **1**:240-241
Rhymes, Mother Goose **4:5-11**
Ride, Sally **3**:186
Rivers, longest **1**:196
Rockets 1:48, 1:71-80; armed, **1**:75
Rocky Mountains **1**:20, **1**:27
Rolfe, John **3**:107
Roman Empire, fall of **3**:53
Roman law **3**:50
Roman numerals **1**:102-103, **1**:224
Romans, thanksgiving feast of **4**:121
Rome, ancient 3:47-51, 3:54, 3:56;
medicine, **1**:171-172
Romulus **3**:49
**Roosevelt, Franklin Delano
3:171-173, 1:236-237**
Roosevelt, Nicholas **3**:143
Roosevelt, Theodore **1**:236-237
Root hairs **2**:15
Roots **2**:14
Rose Bowl football game **4**:102
Rose family **2**:22
Rosh Hashana **4**:130
Rouen, France **4**:137

Royal Society of London **1**:137
Ruggieri, Claude **1**:72
Rules of health 2:173-176
Run of the Bulls **4**:138
Running, in exercises **2**:168-169
Russia 1:17, 3:80-83; Easter in, **4**:108; invasion by Napoleon, **3**:87; see also **Soviet Union**
Russian Revolution Day **4**:140

S

Sacrum **2**:108
Safety rules 2:182-190
Sagas, Viking **3**:64
Saguaro cactus **2**:86
Sahara Desert **1**:197
St. Andrew's Day **4**:142
St. Boniface **4**:123
St. Dominic **4**:139
St. John's Day (Midsummer's Eve) **4**:147
St. Lawrence Seaway **1**:217
St. Nicholas 4:122-123
St. Patrick's Day **4**:142
St. Petersburg (Leningrad) **3**:83
Saliva **2**:128
Salt water communities 2:93-96
Samhain **4**:116-117
Samoa **1**:24
San Antonio Abad **4**:149
San Marino, area of **1**:199
San Salvador **3**:103
Santa Claus 4:122-123
Santa Maria **3**:103
Sap **2**:14
Saprophytes **2**:18
Satellites 1:5, 1:81-84, 1:220
Satellites, weather **1**:38, **1**:83
Saturn 1:58; rings of, **1**:58
Savannah, N.S. **1**:161
Scalp, care of **2**:179
Scandinavia 1:16; holidays, 4:139-140; Vikings, **3**:61-64
Science, future 1:179-183
Scotland **I**:22; Halloween customs, **4**:118-119; **holidays, 4:140-143;** New Year's, **4**:100
Scribes **3**:22

"Sea of Darkness" **3**:99-100
Sea traders, early **3**:38
Seas, largest **1**:198
Seaway, longest **1**:217
Seaweed **2**:95
Secession, of Southern states **3**:152
Seder **4**:132-133
Seed plants **2**:20
Seeds 2:11-12
Senate, U.S. **1**:243
Senses: see **Sight, Hearing, Touch, Taste, Smell**
Sensory nerves **2**:154
Septum **2**:122
Sequoia trees **2**:31-32
Serbia **3**:92
Serfs, Russian **3**:83
Servants, in early cities **3**:22
Seven Sisters (stars) **1**:68
Seven Wonders of the World 1:216
Seville, Spain **4**:138
Shakespeare, William **3**:76
Shepard, Alan B. **3**:183
Shepherds, early Arab 3:57-60
Shigemitsu, Mamoru **3**:177
Shih Huang Ti **3**:36
Shikoku (island) **1**:22
Shiloh, battle of **4**:111
Shinto holidays **4**:155
Ships 3:99-101; atomic-powered, **1**:160-161; Columbus, **3**:103; English warships, **3**:78; Mayflower, **3**:108; **pirates, 3:76, 4:65-69; Spanish Armada, 3:75-79;** Spanish galleon, **3**:78; **steamboats, 3:140-146;** submarine, **1**:126-127; trading, **3**:25, **3**:38; **Viking, 3:61-64**
Ships, sunken **1**:127
Shofar **4**:130
Shooting Match at Nottingham, The **4:55-64**
Shooting stars **1**:62
Sierra Madre mountains **1**:19
Sight 2:114-116
Sikhs **4**:157
"Simon Says" (game) **4**:174
Sinbad the Sailor **3**:60
Singapore **1**:22

Sirius (star) **1**:70
Siva **4**:159
Skeleton 2:101-105; of animals,
    2:48-49
Skin 2:147-150
Skull **2**:106
Sky 1:5-7; **clouds, 1:34; weather,**
    1:33-38
Slavery, early **3**:22; in United States,
    3:123, **3**:151-153
Sleep, need for **2**:174
Smallest animals 2:62-64
Smallest plants 2:27-28
Smallpox **2**:163
Smell 2:122-123
Smith, Captain John 3:105-107
Smoky Mountains **1**:27
Snow **1**:33
Soap, making of **3**:113
Socrates **3**:45
Solar eclipse **1**:52
Solar system 1:39-64; asteroids, **1**:64;
    comets, **1**:60-62; Copernicus, **1**:53;
    exploration of, 1:221; meteors,
    1:62-64; **planets, 1:53-59; sun,**
    1:43-46
Sound 1:154-158; speed of, **1**:157; see
    also **Hearing**
South America 1:10, 1:18; area,
    1:195: Christmas in, **4**:127; Easter
    in, **4**:109; **history, 1:204-209;**
    holidays, 4:145-150; Incas, 3:65-68;
    population, **1**:210
South Carolina **1**:240-241
South China Sea **1**:198
South Dakota **1**:240-241
South Pole **1**:32
Southern Cross (constellation) **1**:70
Soviet Union (Russia) **1**:17; area,
    1:199; **history, 3:80-83; holidays,**
    4:140; population, **1**:210; see also
    Russia
Space, early ideas about **1:39-42;**
    exploration, 1:81-84, **1:220-221;**
    life on other worlds, 1;86-92;
    travel in, 1:93-96, 3:184-186
Space medicine **1**:184
Space probes 1:83, **1**:221

Spain, Christmas in **4**:127; civil war,
    4:138; **holidays, 4:138-139;** war
    with England, **3**:75-79
Spanish Armada 3:75-79
Sparta **3**:42, **3**:46
Spectrum **1**:132
Speech **2**:145
Speedometer **1**:109
Sperm cell **2**:158
Sphagnum (peat moss) **2**:37-38
Spider crab **2**:44
Spinal cord **2**:108, **2**:117
Spine 2:106-108
Spirit of St. Louis **3:167-170**
Sponges **2**:46
Spores **2**:19
Sports, rules of 1:245-262; safety in,
    2:188-190
Spring **4:91**
Spring parties **4**:162
Sputnik I **1**:162
Squanto **3**:109-111
Star cluster **1**:68
Staten Island, N.Y,. **1**:21
States (of U.S.), table of capitals,
    congressional representatives, dates
    of entry into Union, mottoes,
    flowers, birds, nicknames **1**:238-241
Starches **2**:128
Stars 1:5, **1:65-70, 1:**86-87;
    constellations, **1**:40-41; nebulae,
    1:68-69
Statue of Zeus **1**:216
Steamboats, first 3:140-142;
    Mississippi River, 3:143-146
Stegosaurus **2**:58
Stems, plant **2**:15
Stephens, Uriah H. **4**:115
Steppes **2**:82
Stevenson, Robert Louis **4**:65-69, **4**:90
Stomach **2**:128
Storybook party **4**:182
Stratus clouds **1**:34
Streptomycin **1**:121, **2**:38
Submarine **1**:126-127
Suez Canal **1**:217
Sukkoth **4**:121
Sulfa drugs **1**:174

Sumatra **1**:24
Sumer, medicine in **1**:166-167
Summer flounder **2**:42
Summer parties **4**:162
Sun 1:43-46; core, **1**:45; distance
from Earth, **1**:45; eclipse, **1**:52;
flares, **1**:46; gases, **1**:46; radiation,
1:145-147; temperature, **1**:45
Sundial **3**:21, **3**:26
Sunlight **1**:132, **1**:150
Sunspots **1**:46
"Supercold" **1**:179-181
"Superheat" **1**:180
Superstitions **3**:56, **4**:100
Sweat glands **2**:149
Sweden 1:16; holidays, 4:139-140;
Vikings, 3:63
Swimming, safety rules **2**:188
Switzerland **1**:17
Sydney, Australia **1**:25
Synagogue **4**:129
Synapse **2**:153
Syracuse, Greece **1**:123, **1**:128
Syria **1**:14

T

Taft, William Howard **1**:236-237
Tagged atoms **1**:163
Tahiti **1**:24
Takla Makan Desert **1**:197
Talking **2**:145
Taproot **2**:14
Tartars **3**:35
Taste 2:124-126
Taste buds **2**:124, **2**:126
Taurus the Bull (constellation) **1**:40
Taylor, Zachary **1**:236-237
Teeth, care of **2**:180; dentine, **2**:128;
enamel, **2**:128
Tehran, Iran **1**:14
Tel Aviv, Israel **1**:14
Telegraph, invention of 3:148-149
"Telephone" (game) **4**:173
Telescope **1**:48; radiotelescope, **1**:91-92
Temperatures **1**:38, **1**:225; highest
recorded, **1**:200; lowest, **1**:179, **1**:200
Temple of Artemis **1**:216
Temples, ancient **3**:21

Tennessee **1**:240-241
"Tennis, balloon" (game) **4**:173
Terramycin **2**:38
Tetanus **2**:163
Teutons **4**:123
Texas **1**:240-241
Thallophyta **2**:17
"Thank you" notes **4**:190
Thanksgiving Day 4:119-121
Canadian, **4**:144; Pilgrims (first
Thanksgiving), **3**:111
There Was a Little Girl **4**:6
Theseus **3**:40
Thinking process **2**:152
Thirteen colonies (U.S.). **1:235,**
3:115; see also **United States**
Three Golden Apples, The **4:13-18**
Thrust **1**:78
Thrust chamber **1**:78
Thunderhead (cloud) **1**:34
Tigris river **3**:60; cities of, **3**:21
Time, biological **1**:182
Tissues 2:104; fluid, **2**:135
Toad, tree **2**:43
Tobacco **3**:107
Tom Sawyer, Adventures of, selection
4:81-88
Tomb at Halicarnassus **1**:216
Tomb of the Unknowns **4**:112
Tornado **1**:36
Tortoise, desert **2**:88
Touch 2:120-121
Tournament of Roses **4**:102
Tracer atoms **1**:162-163
Trachea **2**:144
Trade winds **1**:35
Traffic signals **2**:187
Trans-Atlantic flight, first
3:167-170
Transfusion, blood **2**:138
Transplants **1**:176
Travel in space 1:93-96
"Treasure Hunt" (game) **4**:174
Tree, Christmas **4**:123
Trees, largest 2:31-33, 1:201; oldest,
1:201, **2**:6; trunks of, **2**:15; **types of**
forests, 1:169-175
Trenton, battle of **3**:125

210

Tribune, Roman **3**:50
Triceps **2**:11
Triceratops **2**:58
Trieste (bathyscaphe) **1**:197
Trigonometry **1**:105
Tropical rain forest 2:78-81
Troy weights **1**:227
Truman, Harry S. **1**:236-237
Tubes, bronchial **2**:144
Tundra 2:72-74
Turks, early **3**:51
Twain, Mark **4**:81-88
Twelfth Night (Jan. 6) **4**:126
Tyler, John **1**:236-237
Tympanic membrane **2**:118
Tyrannosaurus Rex **2**:57

U

Ultrasound **1**:158
Ultraviolet light **1**:151
Umbilical cord **2**:160
UNESCO: see United Nations
    Educational, Scientific and Cultural
    Organization
UNICEF: see United Nations
    Children's Fund
Union of Soviet Socialist Republics
    (U.S.S.R.): see **Soviet Union**
Unions, labor **4**:115
United Nations 3:96, 3:169,
    3:177-179; organizations, 3:178
United Nations Children's Fund **3**:178
United Nations Educational, Scientific
    and Cultural Organization **3**:178
United States of America 1:20,
    1:238-241; area, **1**:199; "birthday,"
    3:187, **4**:112; colonial life,
    3:112-114; **Constitution, 3:127-128;**
    history, Book 3, *America's Story;*
    holidays, 4:99-127; population,
    1:210; **Presidents, 1:236-237;**
    Revolutionary War, 3:117-120,
    3:124-126; statistics, 1:231-243;
    Western settlers, **3**:129; **World War**
    I, 3:92 3:164-165; World War II,
    3:94-95, 3:174-177
United States government 3:116;
    cabinet departments, **1**:242;

divisions of, 1:243-244; executive
    branch, **1**:242; independent
    agencies, **1**:242
Universe: see **Space**
Ural Mountains **1**:10
Uranus 1:58
Urination **2**:131
Utah **1**:240-241
Uterus **2**:160

V

Vaccination **2**:163; vaccines, **1**:121, **1**:176
Valentine's Day parties **4**:185
Valley Forge, Pa. **3**:126, **4**:106
Van Buren, Martin **1**:236-237
Vascular plants **2**:20
Vatican City State, area **1**:199
Veins 2:141-142
Venezuela, holidays in **4**:145
Venice, Italy **1**:21
Ventricles **2**:141
Venus 1:56
Venus VI **1**:84
Vermont **1**:240-241
Vertebrae, spinal **2**:106
Vertebrates 2:45, 2:48-52
Vesta (asteroid) **1**:54
Vibration **1**:154-155
Vicksburg, battle of **3**:157
Victoria, Queen **4**:141
Vietnam **3**:22
Vikings 3:61-64
Villages, early 3:17-18
Villi **2**:129
Vinland **3**:63-64
Vinson-Massif (mountain) **1**:201
Virginia, first settlers **3**:105, state
    information, **1**:240-241
Viruses **2**:161
Vishnu **4**:159
Visvakarma **4**:159
Vitamins 1:177, 2:133, 2:176
Vocal cords **2**:145
Voice box (larynx) **2**:145
Volcanoes 1:9, 1:28-29
Volume 1:122-128; measurement of,
    1:226
Voluntary muscles **2**:112

W

Wales 1:22; holidays, 4:140-143
Walking stick (insect) 2:44
Wall of China, Great 3:34-36
Wallaby 1:24
Walpurgis Night 4:139
Walsh, Lt. Donald 1:197
Wan Hoo 1:72
War of 1812 1:72
War of Secession; see Civil War
Warm Ages 3:12
Warsaw, Poland 1:17
Washington, George 1:236-237, 3:120, 3:124-126, 3:128, 4:112, 4:120, things named after, 4:104
Washington (state) 1:240-241
Washington's Birthday 4:104-106, parties for, 4:183
Water 1:33-38; buoyancy, 1:122-128; chlorination, 1:121; desalination, 1:160; displacement of, 1:124; crosion, 1:30-31; freezing point, 1:38; molecule, 1:116, weather, 1:33-34
Water cycle 1:34
Waterfalls, highest, largest 1:199
Watergate 3:188
Water lilies 2:92
Waterloo, battle of 3:88
Water vapor 1:34, 1:142
Waves, light 1:148-151, 2:114-116
Waves, sound 1:154-158, 2:117-119
Weather 1:33-38
Weather balloons 1:38
Weather satellites 1:38, 1:83
Weight 1:122-128
Weightlessness 1:83
Weights and measures 1:226-227
West, settlers in 3:128, 3:133-136; effect on wildlife, 2:83-84
West Virginia 1:240-241
Westerlies, prevailing 1:35
Whale, blue 2:5, 2:65-67
Whiskey Rebellion 3:128
Whittier, John Greenleaf 4:94-96
Wild West party 4:179-180
Williamsburg, Va. 3:120
Wilson, Woodrow 1:236-237, 3:163-166

Wind 1:33-38
Winter parties 4:162
Wisconsin 1:240-241
Wise Men, Three 4:122, 4:127
Wombat 1:24
Wonder Book for Boys and Girls, selection 4:13-18
"Wonder drugs" 1:174
Wonderful World of Today, The 3:5-16
"Word Treasure Hunts" (game) 4:177
World Health Organization, United Nations 3:178
World history (time line) 1:204-209
World Pen Pals 1:213
World Series Champions 1:251
World War I 3:89-92, 3:163-166
World War II 3:92-95, 3:174-176, 3:177-179
Worms 2:46-47
Wreaths 4:125
Wright, Orville 3:158-162
Wright, Wilbur 3:158-162
Writers, early 3:22
Writing, invention of 3:25
Wynken, Blynken, and Nod 4:92-93
Wyoming 1:240-241

Y

Yangtze River 1:196
Yeast 2:30
Y.M.C.A. 1:213
Yom Kippur 4:130
York, Sergeant Alvin 3:163-166
Yorktown 4:113
Young Men's Christian Association 1:213
Young Women's Christian Association 1:213
Youth organizations 1:212-213
Yu Shui 4:152-153
Yugoslavia 1:17; Christmas in, 4:126
Yule Log 4:126
Y.W.C.A. 1:213

Z

Zeus, statue of 1:216
Zoo party 4:181
Zoologist 3:8

The body type for the four children's volumes in the Home Adventure Library is 14 point Baskerville (Number 353E). This clear, readable face, commonly called English Baskerville, was designed in the eighteenth century by the English type-founder John Baskerville, who based his design on the thick and thin pen strokes in the handwriting of the period. The *Parents' Guide* uses a smaller size of the same type face.

The heads throughout the series are set in Palatino, a Roman-inspired face designed in the 1960's by the German type-founder Hermann Zapf. The type is modern, but follows Renaissance patterns, and is named after the sixteenth-century Italian calligrapher Giambattista Palatino.

The overall design for this series was created and supervised by Ruth Rooney, with the assistance of Don Walkoe, Willis Proudfoot, and Norman Cook. Robert H. Grigg supervised the production.

The editors wish to thank Diane Nelson, of the Association of Medical Illustrators, and Dr. Werner Cryns, who checked the accuracy of illustrations and text in *All About You;* and Thomas J. O'Connor, Jr., coach and teacher at St. Ignatius High School, Chicago, who condensed and adapted the sports rules for the *Fact Book.*